THE BIG THICKET

THE BIG THICKET

a challenge for conservation

dr. pete gunter

photography
roy hamric

JENKINS PUBLISHING COMPANY
Austin and New York

THE CHATHAM PRESS, INC.
Riverside, Connecticut

1971

DISTRIBUTED BY THE VIKING PRESS, INC., NEW YORK

Text and photographs © 1972 by The Jenkins Book Publishing Company, Inc.
Austin and New York
All rights reserved.
Standard Book Number: 85699-044-2
Library of Congress Catalog Card Number: 73-184310
Printed in the United States of America

Design
Larry Smitherman

To Lance Rosier and
Senator Ralph Yarborough

contents

illustrations

foreword

Conservation of America's natural resources is of vital importance to our nation's future. I believe it is imperative that we develop ways to allow Americans to use their resources—*but not to abuse them.*

For this reason, the concerns which Dr. Pete Gunter has raised in his new book, *Big Thicket: A Challenge for Conservation*, are genuine concerns, which government, industry, and individual citizens must respond to.

When we consider the value of a piece of land, like the Big Thicket area, or the beach at Santa Barbara, or the Everglades in Florida, we must never forget to consider this: What is the value of a sunset? What is the value of a walk on the beach, or the right to roam, or the right to simply have a place in nature where man can refresh his spirit? These are things that we cannot buy on the New York Stock Exchange.

I hope that Dr. Gunter's book will be yet another instrument to help awaken 200 million Americans to the fact that they are the stockholders in the "company" we call the United States—and it is up to each and every one of us to insure that our resources are not abused.

Walter J. Hickel

acknowledgments

It is not possible to thank everyone who has in some way or other helped in the writing of this book. Such a list would include half the membership of the Big Thicket Association, plus a good many others. Above all, I owe Lance Rosier more than could ever be repaid for his patient enthusiasm and his limitless store of self-taught knowledge. I am also indebted to Senator Ralph Yarborough for advice and encouragement extending back almost ten years now. Without his insistence this book would never have been written. Further, I would like to thank Geraldine Watson for many hours of informative conversation concerning the *flora* and *fauna* of the Big Thicket.

For information concerning the biological side of the Big Thicket I would also like to thank Dr. Russell Long of Lamar Tech, Dr. Donovan Correll of the Texas Research Foundation, Dr. Claude McLeod of Sam Houston State University, Mrs. Cleve Bachman, Mrs. C. H. Newsom, Mrs. Lynette McGaugh, and a host of botanists, zoologists, and ecologists whose works have proved invaluable, but who can not be footnoted in the text.

To Justice William O. Douglas, Dempsie Henley, and Mary Lasswell I am indebted for some notions of what a book on the Big Thicket should contain.

To Lois Parker of the Lamar University Library I am especially indebted for the opportunity of examining at length the Big Thicket collection there.

To Maxine Johnston I am indebted for abundant hospitality. The same debt is owed Dolly and Lige Hoffman.

Finally, my wife Elizabeth is owed a debt of gratitude for the patience she showed while I pondered obscure texts on ferns, orchids, and the Southeastern Evergreen Forest.

introduction
the long view

The helicopter rose over Kountze, courthouse town of Hardin County. Around us the land spread under the morning sun, hazy and green to a flat horizon. We angled out, following Village Creek down to the Neches River and the Neches River over to Pine Island Bayou, making a big loop that would take us north again on three long trips over the Big Thicket. It would be nearly sundown before we returned from the last trip, with a couple of hundred new photographic negatives in our hands, and the helicopter sound ringing in our ears, and memories of bare clay, bulldozers and smoke plumes to haunt us.

I had hiked the Big Thicket before, following its game trails and sluggish bayous, listening to its silences, its birdcries and leafsounds, watching for orchids, ferns, mushrooms in the black shade of its forest floor. From the helicopter it was entirely different. Up there you had to take the long view, to see things as a whole. You could only conjecture about what lived down there under the dense forest canopy. But about what was happening to the forest as a whole, you could not help seeing. That was why we went up there.

It started out well. The lower Neches River floodplain and the Pine Island Bayou country are two of the least timbered, least civilized parts remaining of the Big Thicket. From the air the country looks like the jungles of Southeast Asia: lush, dense, gnarled, with bayou water glittering in the sun in short stretches between tree overhang. Vines cling to treetops, herons sun on dead branches, magnolia blossoms blaze white against dark green.

Only when we lost the glittering thread of bayou and wandered out over pulp pine plantations did the country change. In the plantations there were straight lines of trees, mile after mile, with nothing but clay, pinestraw and a few grasses in between them. There was no cover for the game, and no food, and the creeks were bulldozed in straight lines like the trees. Ten, fifteen, twenty years ago all of the country down there had been luxuriant forest. Now the plantations were eating up the wilderness, replacing it with wood pulp and biological desert. We turned back again toward the bayou and its deep woods, and forgot—for a while—about pulp pine, and rectilinear creeks.

Gradually, as we traversed and retraversed all of the country which might be included in the proposed Big Thicket National Park, a picture began to take shape. It was a picture of triangles, squares, rectangles, some more than a mile square, others less than thirty acres in extent; it was a picture of jagged scars and new straight roads and grey, irregular patches of dead forest sprayed from the air and left to rot; it was a picture of a wilderness under assault, its flanks gouged and stripped by a bulldozer and buzzsaw technology that knew no limits and brooked no obstacles.

The lumber interests in Texas called the process "reforesting." And in truth, they would return to their new clay prairies to endow them with rows of slash pines. In time also they would return again to spray the rows of pines with chemicals to keep the hardwoods—the oaks, magnolias, hickories, tupelos, elms, birches, maples, beeches—from ever growing there again. In the meantime lumber trucks strained to the highways in record numbers. The big hardwoods disappeared from the once dense backwoods, and those trees that the companies did not want to bother with were piled up in windrows and burned. We could fly from one bulldozed acreage to another by following pillars of smoke as they rose from heaped up matchstick trees and stumps in the morning calm.

Not all the damage was being done by the lumber companies. In one area selected for inclusion in the park (the "triangle" country, south of Saratoga) the bulldozing was being done, apparently, by rice farmers and cattlemen. And, of course, real estate promoters had been drawn by conservationist publicity to put in "red flag" subdivisions where they could cheaply buy a scrap of land. In the triangle country, the day before, we had come upon a subdivision road a half mile long, hidden back in the woods. It was being bulldozed even as lumber company people were trying to "sell" the triangle to the National Park Service as a perfect center for the park.

There was one lumber company, Temple Industries, that was not rooting out hardwoods indiscriminately from its lands. It was locally owned. But the other companies had head offices in New York, Chicago, Toledo, and it was there that the decision to clearcut the Big Thicket was made: there, in the Enlightened North. Probably there also was coined the phrase "reforestation": a semantic triumph masking an ecological disaster. From the air "reforestation" had the look of a last determined rush to pillage a wilderness before it could be protected in the National Park System. Or, if not to pillage *all* of it, then to pillage enough of it so that the resulting park would have to be small. Estimating conservatively, we saw at least twenty-five thousand acres that had been bulldozed out of the deep, rich, ecologically varied woods of the Thicket, in the last two years. The process, moreover, was accelerating. There was still enough wild country left to save. But no wilderness could long stand the pace of that destruction.

When we landed late in the afternoon at the Hardin County Airport, we walked in angry silence to the car. For years the Big Thicket Association, the Audubon Society, the Sierra Club had compromised with the lumber companies, had listened to their claims about "regrowing the Thicket" and being "stewards of the land." Now the facts were as clear as bulldozed clay and burning hardwoods; if we did not begin to fight, there would be nothing left: no game, no birds, no wildflowers, no ferns, no trace of a once great wilderness. Above the hum of apathy and the derision of very vested interests, we would have to make ourselves heard, and understood.

That is what this book is about.

1

deep roots

Long ago, before the conquistadores sailed from Spain or the first pioneers foraged warily into the Appalachians, there sprawled across almost one hundred miles of what is now Southeast Texas a lush semitropical wilderness. The Indians called it the Big Woods. Nearby coastal Indians, the Tonkawas and the Karankawas, and the mound-building Indians to the north, the Caddos, shied away from it. The Big Woods was a no-man's land, a buffer between tribes to its north and south. There were few paths through its deep forests; Indians hunting there journeyed by canoe.

The first Europeans to settle the Southwest were the Spanish. Though they penetrated most of Texas, creating settlements from the Rio Grande to what is now Louisiana, the Spanish seem to have given the Big Woods a wide berth. Their records speak of an immense forest between the missions at Nacogdoches, Texas, and the Gulf, which was impenetrable by land. Only the Indians, it was said, went there. So far as is known, priests and soldiers never followed them.

The first Anglo-Saxon pioneers were drawn to Texas in the 1820's by offers of lavish Spanish land grants. As they moved from Louisiana into Texas, however, they found their way blocked time and again by jungle-like growth and swampy soils along innumerable streams. Frustrated, they turned back, pushing west along the coastal plains to the south and the broken, rolling woods to the north. They called the forbidding country the Big Thicket, and the name stuck. By and large settlers avoided the Big Thicket; the tide of an empire flowed around it, leaving it nearly intact.

By mid nineteenth century legends had grown up around the Big Thicket as luxuriant and strange as its own swamps and jungles. Many of these legends sprang from its reputation as a wilderness sanctuary. Escaped slaves headed there, a step ahead of the

1

baying hounds. Outlaws hid in its canebrakes, bushwhacking unwary travelers. Sam Houston planned to hide his army there, if his attack on the Mexicans at San Jacinto was unsuccessful. As civilization pressed in, the Indians moved there making a last stand against the farmer and the sawmill.

In part the character—and above all the reputation—of the Thicket people stemmed from the fact that the wilderness which they inhabited was initially bordered on the east by the Neutral Ground. The United States and Spain were not able to agree on a boundary between Louisiana and Texas after the Louisiana Purchase. Shortly afterwards a Neutral Ground was created between the Sabine River on the west and Arroyo Hondo on the east, where no settlers were to be permitted. The area soon became a refuge for outlaws, horse thieves, and gamblers. So lawless was the Neutral Ground that from 1810 to 1812 military expeditions were mounted against it. When the United States finally acquired the region in 1821 its bad reputation was firmly established. Many of its inhabitants then moved to the Big Thicket, taking their reputation with them. Tales of murder and mysterious disappearance in the Thicket were common.

Recently in a Thicket sawmill a worker discovered strange marks on a beech tree trunk. The saws were stopped and the log segment retrieved. Deeply engraved in smooth bark was a figure of a man being hanged from a tree. In the foreground were figures of hogs, or cattle. No one knows for certain who was hanged, or when, or why. But sometime, somewhere, back in deep woods, there was almost certainly a hanging, and someone was repaid for his transgressions, whatever they may have been, without benefit of judge or jury. No hint from history or folklore tells us more; the green walls of the Thicket are silent.

During the Civil War draft dodgers and conscientious objectors hid out in the Big Thicket around now-forgotten places, "Blue Hole," "Panther's Den," "Jack Gore Baygall," "Doc Trull Hammock," easily eluding Confederate troops sent in to capture them. Finally a Confederate officer by the name of Kaiser set fire to the woods in an effort to smoke out the deserters. His efforts failed, but for over eighty years nothing would grow on "Kaiser's Burnout," as the scorched one hundred acres came to be known. As late as the First and Second World Wars, descendants of some of the original Civil War holdouts hid out successfully in the deep woods.

The Alabama and Coushatta tribes who were to make the Big Thicket their sanctuary were proud members of the Upper Creek Confederacy. Like other members of that confederacy they had a long history of confrontation with the white man. When the French began establishing outposts along the Gulf of Mexico in the eighteenth century, they found the Alabamas living in villages on the Alabama River at the junction of the Coosa and the Talapoosa Rivers. The State of Alabama and the Alabama River were named after the Alabama Indians who, however, were not to remain there long. The Alabamas fought a long (1702-1713) costly war with the French, but ended by making alliances with them; when the French withdrew to Louisiana in 1763 the Alabamas followed them, settling around Opelousas, in the "Cajun Country." By the beginning of the nineteenth century the Alabamas were again on the move, crossing the border into Texas, where they forged a brief alliance with the Spanish—an alliance which, however, did not prevent them from expressing loyalty to the Americans when occasion required. In the words of Howard N. Martin:

> Dr. John Sibley, the American agent in Nachitoches, Louisiana, also realized the importance of influencing the border Indians. His trading post was a popular gathering point for the Indians in the area. Here the Alabamas and other tribes received gifts and expressed loyalty to the Americans. Then, at the first opportunity, they would travel to Nacogdoches for Spanish gifts and friendship. The Alabamas apparently understood that the Spanish and the Americans were engaged in a tug-of-war for their loyalty, and the Indians capitalized on this conflict in accordance with the opportunities that came their way.

The Indians knew very well what was at stake between the Americans and the Spanish. They had decided long ago the uselessness of armed combat with the ever-numerous white man. Drifting west just ahead of the flood of Anglo-Saxon immigration, they struggled to remain independent by playing one side against the other. When their ancestral woodlands halted at the Texas prairies they halted also, using diplomacy to win redress from the whites.

Redress was not easy to obtain. In 1840 the Republic of Texas granted the Alabamas two leagues of land (8,854 acres) in Tyler County on the northeast border of the Big Thicket. The Indians were soon forced off these lands, however, by belligerent white settlers. In 1854 they were vouchsafed a second plot of 1,110.7 acres, some thirty miles from their original reservation. In 1858 the State of Texas, pressured by local settlers, attempted to move the Alabamas still further west. The tribal chieftains explored the proposed reservation but returned home determined not to be moved. The Lower Brazos Reserve, where they were to be relocated, seemed to them a dreary place compared to the green, rolling hills of Polk County. Moreover, there was good reason to fear for the Alabamas' safety on the proposed reservation. In December, 1858, a group of Texans slaughtered a sleeping camp of peaceful Anadarko and Caddo Indians in the Brazos reservation. The governor of Texas at the time, Hardin R. Runnels, decided that "charity and humanity" forbade him from relocating the Alabamas and exposing them to casual slaughter. They were allowed to remain in the Thicket. For once, fate was on their side.

Like the Alabamas, the Coushattas (or Koasati) were Creeks. The two tribes had long been closely related. Both had fought the French. Both had moved west ahead of the pioneers. Finally, both had settled by the beginning of the nineteenth century in East

Texas, where they maintained commerce with each other. An old legend teaches that the Alabamas and Coushattas came out of the earth on opposite sides of the root of a great tree and settled there in two groups. Their languages are somewhat different, yet mutually intelligible. Doubtless the settlers drew few distinctions between them.

Around 1830 the Coushattas had attained the peak of their development in Texas. Their three villages near the Trinity River in Polk County had attained a combined population of 600; farming, hunting, and trading with the white man had made them prosperous. By 1840, however, white settlers began claiming their lands and village life deteriorated. The inhabitants of two Indian settlements (Long King's Village and Battise Village) were forced either to wander the woods, subject to instant eviction by white landlords, or to settle at the one remaining village (Colita's Village, north of the town of Romayor). In 1840 the Coushattas were granted two leagues of land by the Republic of Texas. By the time the land was surveyed and field notes filed, however, white men had already claimed it. In 1859 most of the Coushattas were allowed to settle with their Alabama kinsmen. In 1885 the State of Texas granted the Coushattas 665 acres. This grant also remained a paper benefaction, since land suitable for a reservation could no longer be found in Polk County. In 1906 the last free Coushattas were moved to the Alabama reservation in Polk County.

Years of poverty were to follow. The woodland Indians had no training in large-scale agriculture, which the sandy hill soil of their reservation would scarcely have supported anyhow. Had they wished to timber their lands, moreover, their acreage would have been too small to support the tribe. Even during periods of intense hunger the Alabamas and Coushattas refused to cut their timber, which today constitutes one of the few stands of virgin forest in the Thicket. Many of both Texas' and North America's largest trees in their species are found in the rich bottomlands of the Alabama and Coushatta reservation.

The white man had early sent his churches to the reservation, presumably to teach the Indians what decency is. Under the combined impact of poverty and an alien (to them) religion, Indian culture began to disintegrate as the Indian village sank into lassitude. By the 1920's the condition of the Alabamas and Coushattas had deteriorated so markedly that the State of Texas was moved to "do something for them." In 1928 3,071 acres of new land were purchased for them with federal funds. Most accounts of this lavish transaction fail to record that the land was first cleared of all valuable timber before being bestowed. From 1928 to 1933 seventy-two tin roofed shacks were built "to get the Indians out of their log cabins." Today it is claimed by some Alabamas and Coushattas that as many as half their tribes died of starvation on the reservation. Probably no one will ever know for certain. The dead do not speak, and the reservation's administrators deny the claim.

In the original Big Thicket were prairies populated with wild horses and longhorn

7

cattle, sandy savannahs where horseback settlers hunted wild hogs, canebrakes miles in length, flower-carpeted meadows, swamps too deep to timber and land that, suitably coaxed, would bring in a good cotton crop. Not all of the Thicket, therefore, was lumbermen's country. And yet, the prime source of change in the region was to be, and still is, the timber industry.

The first timbering in the Thicket began in the decade 1850-1860. Most of the pine and cypress cut during these years were floated down the Sabine and Neches Rivers. The East Texas Railroad, which might have been extended into the Thicket, was dismantled and fed into the Confederate war effort, with the result that no railroad was built into the region until well after the Civil War. Not till the 1880's did railroads open the Big Thicket for logging. Most of these, the Houston-East and West-Texas, the Sabine and East Texas, the Trinity and Sabine, concentrated on the western reaches of the great wilderness. In the mid 1890's another period of railroad building began, however, in the eastern Thicket. Branching out from the main railroad lines were smaller, trunk lines, so that the entire region was traversed with networks of tracks, almost all of which have now been abandoned and given back to wilderness. One searches in vain in the ensuing cutting for a big tree saved, a last grove of virgin pine or tupelo bypassed, a spasmodic effort to respect the general ecology of the region. When the lumber companies cut, they took every saleable item and left wreckage. In the words of Professor C. A. McLeod:

> ... by the beginning of the 1900's, the Big Thicket loblolly pine-hardwood forest, the adjacent shortleaf pine-hardwood forest to the west and north, and the magnificent longleaf pine forest contiguous on the northeast and east were under sustained assault that was not to end until practically all of the virgin pine forests were reduced to cut-over woodlands.

Speaking with the wisdom of hindsight it is easy for us to point out that if a single acre of Thicket ground had been left uncut for every ten thousand acres timbered, those scattered acre plots would today contain trees of incredible size and beauty. Pioneer mentality, however, left little room for farsighted speculations. The trees fell. And some men, a few, became rich from it.

Thicket settlers did not always get along well with the lumber companies. A cursory glance over area maps reveals many burned places in the woods (Dunnie Burnout, Old Hat Burnout) not connected with Captain Kaiser. Some of these witness a hunter's attempt to smoke a bear or panther out of hiding. Others, however, represent some settler's last revenge against a lumber company which had seized his lands. The story of land acquisition by early lumbermen has, one is told, yet to be written. That it has not been written can be explained by the fear of lawsuits or perhaps worse. Lumbermen, with the aid of a strong infusion of northern capital, took advantage of Texas' "use and possession" laws to seize land that had been in settlers' families for generations. Often the trees had been leveled before the damage was found. Protesting settlers were met at the courthouse by corporation lawyers quoting obscure texts and promising to strike back with expensive court trials. I have heard it said more than once by those who claim they dare not write about it, that most of the land owned by big lumber companies in the Thicket was stolen, pure and simple. Perhaps that is an exaggeration. In any case, the settlers might well have won their case if they had stuck together and persisted. But by their very character they could not bring themselves to do so.

The most famous of the old lumber barons was a man by the name of John Henry Kirby. By the second decade of the twentieth century he dominated not only the Texas lumber industry but the entire Southern industry as well. In addition to several million acres of piney woods in East Texas, Kirby in 1906 operated twelve different sawmills (at Beaumont, Call, Fuqua, Bronson, Roganville, Woodville, Mobile, Bessmay, Browndell, Kirbyville, and Evadale) with a combined capacity of 1,445,000 board feet per day.

From the period of the First World War through the 1930's the East Texas pineries were troubled by labor unrest. Kirby's approach to the workers of his company towns could be deeply moving at times, particularly when it appeared that they were about to go out on strike:

> I am talking for the man who has a wife and babies at home, the man who, perhaps, has been visited by misfortune, the man who may not be a good manager, the man whose meal barrel is not full and who could not stand a shutdown. It is in his behalf that I would ask his fellow laborers not to push upon him conditions that will destroy him and bring tears to the cheek of his good wife, anxiety to both their hearts and distress and hunger to the little ones who toddle about their home.

He would close down his mills immediately, Kirby added, if the Brotherhood of Timber Workers were to make demands on the mill operators—any demands at all. The long-term results of lumber company attitudes were predictable, given the isolation and relative poverty of company towns, the friction between black and white lumber workers, and the inbred paternalism of the South. Unionism was slow to enter the piney woods, and the salaries, living conditions, and educational levels of the East Texas lumber workers lagged far behind those of lumber workers in other parts of the country. The company town and the company-owned county (65 percent of the land in Hardin County and over 80 percent of the land in Tyler County, for example, is lumber company owned) have had a lasting influence on the politics in East Texas. Maps showing those counties having remarkably low per capita income and maps showing those counties in which lumber companies are the largest employers show a considerable degree of overlap.

Never have men so quickly and ruthlessly slashed a forest as they did the Southern pine forests. Labor was cheap, the country flat to gently rolling, the weather rarely

11

severe. The Southern lumber baron pushed his "cut and get out" policy to an extreme not seen before or since. Oddly enough, very little lore resulted from this massive transformation. The lumberjack of the north and northwest has no counterpart in Texas mythology. Compared with the backwoods bear hunter, the cowboy, or the oilfield roughneck, the East Texas timber worker appears as drab a character as the Southern mill worker he in part resembles, tied to the region in which he, his wife, and children were born, constantly in debt to the company store.

In the 1880's and 90's the Thicket became famous for its epic bear hunts, and its hunters and their dogs became, for a time, celebrities with a statewide and even a national audience. America's most renowned bear and panther hunter, Ben Lilly, was drawn to the Big Thicket before heading west to the last frontiers of the Rocky Mountains. It is said that Lilly killed his 118th bear in the Thicket—one of the largest black bears, incidentally, ever killed in North America. Old-timers can still remember how Lilly could keep his sense of direction in the deepest woods, how he could climb full speed to the top of a tall tree or jump flat-footed out of a barrel.

In the early twentieth century, when the last of the big bear hunts were taking place, the Thicket became the scene of an oil rush. The first well was drilled near Beaumont, at Spindletop; subsequent discoveries along the lower margins of the Big Thicket at Sour Lake (1901), Saratoga (1903), and Batson (1904) transformed once isolated crossroads into roaring, chaotic boomtowns, knee-deep in mud, drilling rigs, tent saloons, and tough opportunists from the four corners of the earth.

Oil was nothing new to the Thicket, whose southern region has more than its share of oil seeps, warm sulphur springs, and salt domes. Indians had long used oil seep water from the Thicket for medicine, and stories about secret oil springs and Indian cures were current among early pioneers. The tip-off came when settlers loosed their hogs into the woods only to find them returning covered from snout to foot with black, viscous fluid. The hogs had used the oil springs as wallows; the settlers, in turn, followed the hogs to the springs and bottled the contents as medicine. In 1869 the first oil well in Texas was drilled in Saratoga. The drilling equipment was ingenious. A pine trunk with a heavy weight on one end was cantilevered over a second pine tree tunk and allowed to drop on the oil pipe, which was driven into the ground in much the same way as a nail is driven into a board with a hammer. When a pipe was driven in, a new pipe length was added and the hammering would begin again. The resulting well, in spite of the genius invested in its creation, was not a success. An early oil boom, like the sustained timbering of the last wilderness, was forestalled thirty years by a stroke of chance.

Oil interests, early or late, have taken little more interest in preserving America's ecological balance than the lumbermen who preceded them. In the Thicket the overflow of oil and salt water from oil wells has killed big cypress trees along creeks and marshes and destroyed the nesting places of countless water birds. No one has ever mapped the acres of dead trees left by the careless construction and maintenance of wells and storage tanks there, but it would make a large, depressing map. There are no laws to constrain pipeline companies from bulldozing pipelines wherever they please. What conservationists face in combatting pipeline damage in Alaska now can be seen by casually observing what pipelines have done in the Big Thicket in the past.

Of course, not every transformation of the Big Thicket effected by the oil companies can be charged to their neglect. One case in point is the Texas Company's Fee No. 4603, Brooks Subdivision, part of the original Sour Lake oil field. On October 7, 1929, a very ordinary incident gave warning that something out of the ordinary was about to occur: two Texas Company wells that had been producing oil began suddenly to pump water. The next morning members of the "bull gang" on another Texaco well noticed something wrong. A spot which used to be one hundred feet from their well "wasn't where it used to be." The ground had sunk slightly, and was continuing to settle. At first the movement was so slow that it was hardly noticeable. An area about the size of a suburban lot gave way slowly as if pulled down by some invisible force. The crew apprehensively moved the derrick and equipment away as the earth sank. Water quickly filled the depression as trees and all other vegetation on the spot began to disappear. By nightfall good-sized trees had vanished, still standing upright. As the crater widened, water from a nearby creek began to drain into it. Huge fissures along its edge began pointing toward adjacent oil storage tanks. A recently completed well with a daily flow of 250 barrels started gushing salt water and the next day quit altogether. Oilmen looked on apprehensively, hypnotized by the relentless collapse. By the third day the sink reached a depth of 140 feet (well below sea level) and covered almost fifteen acres. Then, as suddenly and as mysteriously as it began, the subsidence stopped, leaving a small lake and thirty-five failed oil wells. Only one well, the Gilbert 89 just west of the sink, was improved by its experience. Originally pumping ten barrels a day, it spurted suddenly to 250. Production was never restored in the other thirty-five wells. The Texas Company pumped one for two years and brought up nothing but salt water.

For several days the sink was front-page news as photographers, geologists, and curiosity seekers crowded its edges. A half dozen theories were created to explain it. The sinking was the "changing of cap rock formations and oil sands"; it was caused by heavy blasting in the area to locate a salt dome; water in the cap rock dissolved the salts of the dome; a cavity was created by the removal of 73 million barrels of oil from the field over the last quarter of a century; or a cavity was created by the removal of salt in connection with oil well drilling. In a learned paper presented before the American Institute of Mining Engineers, Dr. E. H. Sellards suggested that the removal of underlying salt was probably the cause of the sink. But he admitted that no one would ever know for certain. Nearby Sour Lake (the body of water, not the town) had probably been formed in the same way; but that was long before anyone had ever thought of drilling oil wells there. In

the meantime the crater lake remained, a dead sea gradually filling in, another enigma for the Thicket people to ponder.

The oil field boom vanished even more quickly than the lumber railroads and jackleg lumber mills. Small towns lapsed back into obscurity as oil field workers left. Even the trains ran less often. The second-growth lumber regrew. The Big Thicket fell off into a sleep that lasted forty years, a sleep from which it is only now awaking.

Today, off on the gravel roads that turn into dirt roads and tire tracks through tall grass, you may still find cabins where electricity is rejected in favor of coal oil lamps and a way of life continues little different from that of the nineteenth-century pioneer. But, like the Appalachian mountaineer, today the Thicket backwoodsman fights a losing battle with the bulldozer, the chain saw, and something still more nebulous, which undermines inherited ways of seeing things and transforms what men will allow themselves to believe.

I remember a drive through the Big Thicket some eight years ago to photograph log cabins. The cabins were there, along with the old men whittling in the shade and women in poke bonnets hoeing weeds. But some of the cabins had been "updated." My favorite was set far back in a secluded clearing: a salmon pink log cabin with a twenty-foot television antenna.

It is a tribute to the fecund richness of the region that the Big Thicket remains today a distinct biological entity. If this chronicle has made it seem that with the waning of the first decades of the twentieth century little was left of the wilderness but a forest of stumps, it has been misleading. Virgin areas still remain, often on land too swampy and remote to cut at a profit or on plots entangled in litigation. In still other areas the region's phenomenal growth rate has ensured the appearance of second-growth forests approaching the Thicket's earlier botanical exuberance. There is still time, conservationists argue, to save what is left of the Thicket for the future, to prevent it from becoming a leveled-off biological scrap heap, a patchwork of barren pine plantations, polluted streams and vacation subdivisions. But in order to explain why the Big Thicket is a candidate for wilderness conservation, it is necessary to explain what exists there. What is there about the Thicket that so excites the biologist, the ecologist, the bird expert, the hiker? The answer is as complex as the Thicket itself—and as interesting.

2

inventory of an anomaly

You can find anything in there," the old settlers used to say, "from a cricket to an elephant." While no one has yet found an elephant in the Thicket, the settlers were basically correct. In fact, they said far more than they knew. The Big Thicket is the Biological Crossroads of North America. It contains both temperate and subtropical plants and animals, along with a strong infusion of species from the dry treeless west. That such diverse living things should exist together in one ecosystem is highly interesting; that they should flourish there in such size and abundance is more remarkable still. In the Thicket there are many varieties of orchids; but there are also tumbleweed and cacti. Where else, one wonders, will one find roadrunners alongside alligators, mesquite and yucca alongside cypress and water tupelo?

In spite of the uniqueness of the Big Thicket, it has received little intensive and systematic study. The last thorough inventory, the *Biological Survey of the East Texas Big Thicket Area*, was completed in 1938. Since then new plants and animals have entered the Thicket and, almost certainly, others have become extinct. The extent of the changes are, moreover, difficult to trace in an area so large and varied. Even were the *Biological Survey* still entirely accurate in its catalogue, it is by its own admission incomplete. The insect and fish life of the region is almost wholly unresearched and is certain to contain some surprises. The same is true of its molds, algae, fungi, lichens, and mosses. In fact, there is not a single category examined in the *Biological Survey*, from slime molds through migratory waterfowl, which can be declared final. Whoever writes, lectures, talks or just plain dreams about the Big Thicket's standing inventory of life-forms had best tread warily. It is too easy to create fiction in place of fact—almost as easy as it is to deny a fact because it doesn't fit one's fictions.

19

There were reports, around the turn of the century, of ocelots ("leopard cats") being found in the Thicket. It is thoroughly unlikely that one would find them there now; the nearest known ocelots are in Texas along the Rio Grande River, hundreds of miles away. I have argued with biologists who claim that it is impossible that the ocelot could have ever lived in the Thicket at all. Doubtless those initial reports concerned overgrown painted housecats. And the same holds for the Mexican jaguars which settlers once claimed were there too: even though both jaguars and ocelots are known to have ranged once as far east as Arkansas and Louisiana.

Beside the animal species which no longer exist in the region, there are some which are near extinction. There are still occasional reports of panthers being seen—and heard—in the Thicket. Visible panthers in the area are almost always said to be black, while auditory panthers are said to sound like a screaming woman. Legends about black panthers, incidentally, are by no means to be discarded as false simply because most panthers are brownish-grey. Biologists have recently discovered that warm, wet climates have a direct effect on the coloration of many species of animals—panthers included. It has probably been fifteen or twenty years since a *bona fide*, vouched-for panther sighting. There is good reason, however, to hope that the bear is making a comeback in the Thicket. The Louisiana black bear is slowly finding its way back into East Texas generally as land formerly in cotton has been gradually turned back into woods and tree farms, and former tenant farmers have left the land for the greener pastures of the town and city. When a bear wandered into Livingston, Texas, in the late 1950's it was thought to be the very last bear in the Thicket. Doubtless that is why the local citizens killed the animal and barbecued it. It weighed, I am told, 458 pounds and tasted kind of "gamey." Today there may be some bear in the general Thicket region in spite of local environmental noncon-science.

There are alligators in the Big Thicket too. For certain there is at least one, which escaped from its pen in the Alabama and Coushatta reservation in the spring of 1970 and meandered down into Big Sandy Creek. I am sure many of the Indians would have liked to go with it, to get away from the tourists.

There are some alligators farther down Big Sandy Creek, as there are in the swamps along the Neches River. Occasional ponds in the Big Thicket may still shelter a few. None of these, however, will survive the continuing inroads of poachers and the bulldozing of streams and swamps that have marked the last two decades of Big Thicket history. I have heard of fourteen-foot alligators being captured in the region since the 1940's. That is "champion" size for an alligator, but I doubt whether any that big could be found today.

The Thicket is not the only place where the big reptiles have been faced with extinction. Alligators have been for so long the victims of poaching that for a while it looked as if their existence might be threatened even in the Florida Everglades. Recent laws forbidding shipment of alligator hides across state lines have made alligator poaching unprofitable, however, and the big reptiles are increasing in number for the first time since European explorers set foot on the North American continent. That this is so is no small matter for wilderness ecology. Alligators, by constant digging, manage to keep their water holes from going dry during the hot summer months, thereby assuring a water supply for other game. With luck, and protection, they could begin to increase in numbers again in the sloughs and marshes of the Big Thicket.

Big, meat-eating animals are spectacular, both because they frighten us and because their existence seems conclusive proof of the wilderness character and remoteness of an area. It takes more than an occasional bear or panther, however, to constitute a wilderness. The Thicket's wilderness status is equally evidenced by the fact that it contains more than its share of smaller animals of the South and Southwest. The wildcat is there, along with the coyote and the Texas red wolf—a smaller relative of the grey wolf of the western plains. The Texas red wolf, incidentally, has so interbred with the coyote that its continued existence as a distinct species is increasingly precarious. One of the last breeding grounds of the purebred red wolf is on the prairies of Liberty County, just south of the present Thicket. The red wolf is occasionally seen in the woods of Hardin and Polk counties. If it is to survive, it must have the Big Thicket as a last sanctuary.

Hunters have long realized the Thicket's function as a sanctuary for deer, which continue to thrive in its woods—or would, if game laws were applied there consistently. (They have only begun to be applied at all since around 1964.) And, of course, there are the usual small animals found in Southern woodlands: beaver, mink, otter, nutria, muskrat, red and grey fox, flying squirrel, raccoon, opossum, cat squirrel and grey squirrel, and the omnipresent armadillo. The ring-tailed cat, a racoon-like carnivore of the western deserts, has recently been found in the Big Thicket, in Hardin County. Perhaps it too, like the armadillo, is expanding its range into the green, well-watered country to the east.

To this list must be added at least two real oddities. The first is a monkey colony found in the Thicket in the fall of 1966. What the monkeys were doing there, or whether they survived the winter, is not known. A boy shot one of them and brought it to Beaumont to display. It was a squirrel monkey, full-grown. He had to shoot one and bring it back, the boy said, or no one would believe him.

Just as peculiar as the tales of monkey colonies in the Thicket is a story recounted by Dempsie Henley in his *The Murder of Silence.* A friend of Henley's, a Houston businessman, was given a big black Australian wolfhound as a present. The wolfhound apparently did not take to suburban living, however, and the businessman finally brought it to the Big Thicket and set it free. The dog loped around the car several times and then headed warily out into the woods. The businessman headed back to Houston, much relieved. Recently, however, remote settlers have reported that a huge black dog has been seen around their cabins. It is leading a wolfpack. Perhaps this explains the difficulties of

an elderly lady who lives in the hotel at the abandoned town of Bragg, in Hardin County. She has had to start feeding her dogs indoors lately, she complains. When she tries to feed them outdoors, the wolves eat the dogfood off the back steps.

The last two times I visited the Big Thicket backwoods along Pine Island Bayou I met a man riding on a pony and blowing a tin horn. The man explained that he had lost his dogs while hunting and that he had been out looking for them now every day for a couple of weeks. He had, the man explained, about given up any hope of finding them. Probably they are still out there in the Thicket somewhere, running game.

A couple of years ago Lance Rosier told a reporter from an Eastern newspaper of three or four dozen jackasses that had been turned loose in the woods by a local stockman to run wild. Conceivably the hunter's dogs are chasing the stockman's wild jackasses. Stories like these convince me that anyone who tells you that he knows exactly what he will find when he hikes out into the Thicket is a liar.

The two-legged hairless ape ought to be mentioned in any Thicket inventory. Of this species, the most spectacular are those which hide in the deep woods seeking sanctuary from the outer world. The most famous of these is the Nude Man of the Big Thicket, who lived there in the 1950's. Several people had glimpsed the man. Then one fine day, a Mr. Sutton encountered him on a lonely road. The hermit announced that if anyone wanted to come in after him they'd have to come in shooting. He was a large man, deeply tanned and hairy, with a long beard. He had a gun in each hand, and was naked. So far as is known, no one "went in after him" though there are stories of the subsequent capture of an escaped mental patient who had lived for nine years in the Thicket on wild fruits and armadillo. Whether the two hermits are one and the same is—well, as usual, the facts get a little vague on that point.

In 1938 a bank robber and murderer by the name of Red Goldman stole a cab in Houston and retreated to his native Big Thicket to hide out. Old-timers in the area will tell you that it was a weird sight to see Goldman cutting down some back road in his cab at night, his roof lights glowing against blackness. A man in a cab in a wilderness area is not exactly inconspicuous; but Goldman managed to hide out for three months in the Big Thicket without getting caught (or overcharging a fare, either). It was not until the sheriffs, and deputies of both Hardin and Jefferson counties got together and cashed in on a tip that the outlaw was caught and riddled with bullets in the corncrib back of his mother's house. For some years the corncrib was a sort of local tourist attraction, until the novelty of it wore off.

The other two-legged creatures in the Thicket are the birds. Compared to man they are generally more graceful; and, with few exceptions, they are a great deal less dangerous. There are at least three hundred species of birds in the region, give or take a few dozen. More than one hundred are year-round residents, the rest are migratory. The number of migratory birds is significant: the region is one of the most important stopping-points for migrating birds along the Gulf Coast. It may be that the Thicket is as equally important for its function as a migratory haven as it is a permanent sanctuary for rare birds.

A list of three hundred species may not in itself appear impressive. The number of bird species known to occur in the United States, however, is about 720, while the number known to occur in Texas is approximately 540. The significance of this last figure becomes apparent when it is realized that the State of California, which has the second largest species count in the nation, has only 439 varieties of birds. The Big Thicket thus contains more than one-third of the bird species of the United States and more than half the species found in Texas. Very few states—only a handful—shelter as many bird species as the three or four hundred thousand acres of the Big Thicket.

Unfortunately, there is no official check list of Big Thicket bird life. Olin Pettingill laments in his *Guide to Bird Finding West of the Mississippi*:

> Northwest of industrial Beaumont, with its factories and refineries and its oak-and-magnolia-shaded residential districts, sprawls the BIG THICKET, a wilderness area estimated to cover some two million acres. Why, considering its extent, its fascinating complexity of terrain and plant distribution, and its reputed richness in birdlife, it remains an unknown quantity ornithologically cannot be answered.

Pettingill's remarks, while less appropriate today than when they were written in 1953, still contain a certain validity. The Thicket bird life remains to be certified in detail. What follows, therefore, is in part an estimate; it is based both on the known general distribution of some species and specific sightings of others.

One would not ordinarily expect to see a woodpecker as big as a hawk. The ivory-billed woodpecker, however, achieves this distinction: achieves it, that is, if it indeed still exists. For the ivory-bill, which once ranged from the Gulf of Mexico as far as North Carolina and southern Indiana, is now thought to be extinct. One of its last possible habitats is the Big Thicket where, from time to time, it is reported by ardent bird-watchers, only to disappear when photographers converge to make definite identification. Two factors have determined the precarious status of the big woodpeckers. The most obvious is the disappearance of the virgin woodlands upon which they depend. Almost as fateful, however, is the bird's size and striking appearance. With its overall body length of twenty-one inches (compared to the sparrow hawk at eleven, the broad-winged hawk at eighteen, the duck hawk at nineteen, the chicken hawk at twenty inches) and flamboyant black, white and red markings, it has evoked such awestruck names as "goodgod," "mygod," "godamighty." It has also evoked the pride of backwoods marksmen, who have made it a favorite target.

The elusiveness of the ivory-bill is matched only by its strength and vigor. A

naturalist who wounded one and confined it to his hotel room, in Wilmington, North Carolina, wrote:

> In less than an hour I returned, and, on opening the door he set up a distressed shout, which appeared to proceed from grief that he had been discovered in his attempts to escape. He had mounted along the side of the window, nearly as high as the ceiling, a little below which he began to break through. The bed was covered with large pieces of plaster, the lath was exposed for at least fifteen inches square, and a hole large enough to admit the fist opened to the weather-boards; so that, in less than an hour he certainly would have succeeded in making his way through.

The ivory-bill is also a strong flyer, capable of ranging easily over an area thirty or forty miles in width. It is scarcely any wonder that a given locale should fail to yield more than one sighting; an hour after the initial sighting the big, shy bird may be many miles away.

Around four years ago a grizzled backwoodsman walked into the office of Archer Fullingim, editor of the *Kountze News*. The man asked Archer whether he thought there were any of those ivory-billed birds like the ones whose pictures had been run in the newspaper. When Archer replied skeptically the man reached around and dumped a dead ivory-billed woodpecker on the editorial desk. The editor of the *Kountze News* stared in dismay and unbelief. "Those birds are out on my place," the settler grinned. "They're the rarest birds in the world, and I've got 'em. Ain't nobody but me know where they are." The man pocketed the bird in his jacket and walked out, remarking that there were "plenty more where that one came from." Fullingim learned later, however, that the man had seen no more ivory-bills. They deserted the man's land, seeking, no doubt, a deeper solitude somewhere in the Thicket.

Would-be discoverers of the ivory-bill also have to cope with a second problem. If one did sight an ivory-bill, they argue, it is as certain as sunrise that the experts would insist it was only a pileated woodpecker. Around the turn of the century ornithologists were mournfully sure that the pileated woodpecker would follow the ivory-bill into extinction as tracts of virgin wilderness vanished from once-remote Southern woodlands. Fortunately, the pileated woodpecker has managed to adapt, with notable success, to cutover woodlands. Like the ivory-bill, but smaller (having a maximum body length of nineteen inches), the pileated woodpecker is a bird of remote, little frequented places. That it exists in the Thicket is a tribute to the depth and solitude of its woods.

Three other rare birds, Bachman's warbler, the brown-headed nuthatch, and the red-cockaded woodpecker, are found in the Thicket, along with the golden eagle, which regularly manages to get shot by local hunters. Since the golden eagle is declining rapidly in numbers and range, perhaps it is not too much to suggest that it be protected in the Big Thicket, along with its endangered bird relatives.

The red-cockaded woodpecker provides a classic case of a bird whose existence is

27

threatened by radical changes in its habitat. A comparatively small bird about seven inches long, it sports a zebra-striped ladder back, a black crown and a large white face patch—one of its prime identification marks. Unfortunately, the red-cockaded woodpecker will nest only in two sorts of trees, the loblolly pine or the shortleaf pine. There is no shortage of either of these in the deep South, nor is any shortage projected. But the scarce woodpeckers will nest in one of these trees only if it has the "red-heart disease"—a plant illness carried by airborne fungi. It is precisely the rotting red-heart pine which modern lumber companies cull out of their forests to make room for healthier trees. The birds are so bound by instinct to this type of tree that they are unable to adapt to any other. Destruction of the nesting-places of the red-cockaded woodpecker will mean its certain extinction.

Besides rare birds, the region serves as a refuge and nesting place for large numbers of water birds. Wherever one hikes in the Thicket he is sure to surprise some water birds, foraging along a slough or backwater or perching silently on a cypress knee or outstretched limb. Among these are herons, egrets, roseate spoonbills, cormorants, coots, rails, bitterns, yellowlegs, and ibises, American's only species of stork. An interesting recent immigrant is the cattle egret, which has wended its way to the Gulf states from North Africa. To this catalogue of birds must be added seven kinds of owls, at least thirteen varieties of hawks, one species of eagle, thirty-six sorts of warblers, seventeen kinds of sparrows and, to recur for a moment to the ivory-bill, nine of Texas' fourteen species of woodpeckers. The number of warblers in this list is particularly striking. The Big Thicket contains three-fifths of North America's fifty-four varieties of wood warblers, and almost four-fifths of the warblers species (forty-eight) found in Texas. Some of these, like Swainson's warbler and the Connecticut warbler, are scarce birds; Bachman's warbler, already mentioned above, is very rare. The list of Thicket birds could be greatly extended, to include ducks, geese, vireos, flycatchers, migrant shore birds and many others. But the point has been made. The Big Thicket is a remarkably rich bird sanctuary; it is one of North America's significant ornithological resources.

Texas is one of the last places on earth where most people would ordinarily go looking for trees: mesquite perhaps and sagebrush, but not trees. The part of Texas covered by the Big Thicket, however, receives between fifty and sixty-five inches of rainfall annually—a characteristic which it shares with much of Louisiana and Florida. When this is coupled with sandy, water-storing soils, the results are as impressive as they are predictable: huge trees, some of which are the world's largest in their species.

The cataloguing of big trees is a relatively recent practice. It was begun by the American Forestry Association in 1940 as an attempt "to halt the tragic disappearance of America's most magnificent tree specimens." Unlike certain other good ideas, it has managed to work. "Champion" trees (i.e., the largest of their species) are now sought out and given publicity and a title. Through the competition to seek out and establish new state and local champions, people who once could not have cared less about trees have gone out of their way to preserve and protect local giants and near-giants. The search for prestigious tree champions provides one of the few instances in which the competitive spirit has had a positive effect on nature.

If the Thicket counties as described in the Thicket *Biological Survey* are taken into account, the following list (valid as of January 1, 1971) emerges. Of the one hundred and ten species listed, fifty-six Texas state champions fall within the borders of the original Thicket. Of these, fifteen are national champions: common crape myrtle, black hickory, American holly, Texas honeylocust, Rugel sugar maple, pyramid magnolia, blue-jack oak, longleaf pine, redbay, western soapberry, tree sparkleberry, sweetbay magnolia, Chinese tallowtree, water tupelo, and yaupon. Interestingly, four of these reach record size at the far western edge of the distribution of their species. A fifth, the pyramid magnolia, does not normally occur west of Louisiana.

Unfortunately, a champion tree, like a professional athlete or a pop musician, is likely to go quickly out of style as new champions are found. Water elm, planertree, sweetbay, sugar hackberry, common sweetleaf, Allegheny chinkapin, two-winged silver-bell, eastern redcedar and sugarberry in the Thicket have recently been demoted from the status of national champions to that of near-champions. Not more than four years ago the world's tallest cypress was found in a baygall in the Trinity River bottomlands; two years later a second cypress was found a mile north of the world's tallest, having almost the same dimensions. A still larger cypress stands further back in the swamps. No one has trekked in to measure it. Oil well overflow killed it long ago.

In reading through the list of trees included in the 1938 biological survey, it is interesting to note the number of species catalogued which normally do not range as far east, west, or south as the Thicket. The silver maple and northern red oak do not normally range as far south as the Big Thicket. The cucumber tree is assumed not to range as far west as East Texas. The nutmeg hickory is presumed to range no closer to the Thicket than Mississippi and southern Arkansas. The rock chestnut oak is commonly found no farther south or west than the Appalachian mountains. The Ohio buckeye's range is assumed to reach no closer to the Thicket than Northeast Texas, where it is an intruder from Arkansas and Oklahoma, while the northern catalpa ought never to appear in East Texas at all. The wavyleaf oak ranges over Nevada and Colorado, and far West Texas; western walnut and Mexican persimmon are trees of dry Southwest Texas, not of East Texas; the speckled alder ranges no farther south than Pennsylvania and Nebraska.

Some of these trees were doubtless brought to the Thicket long ago from far outside its boundaries and planted, or set free. (You will, for example, find mimosas and Chinese tallow trees growing wild in the area; but no one will tell you that these asiatic plants originated in Southeast Texas.) It is unlikely, however, that all of these were introduced from elsewhere, so the question naturally arises: What are they doing in the

29

Big Thicket? It is an interesting question to ponder.

The animals, birds, and trees catalogued so far are perhaps the most striking features of the Big Thicket area. The catalogue as it now stands, however, is by no means complete. At least three more categories (animal and vegetable, but not mineral) should be added—though even these will not make the inventory exhaustive. The snakes of the Thicket deserve to be mentioned. Its wildflowers merit a survey of their own (and not just for contrast, either). Finally, the most unglamorous subject I can think of—the molds and fungi—rate a brief discussion. All those who are repelled by reptiles can skip the next few paragraphs and go on to the section on wild orchids and azaleas.

The North American continent has four varieties of poisonous snakes, and the Thicket has them all: coral snakes, water moccasins, copperheads, and at least four varieties of rattlesnake. You would probably have to work overtime to be bitten by any one of these, however, since all of North America's poisonous snakes would rather run than fight, if given a chance. You would have to step right on top of any one of them to get a bite under most circumstances. (I have heard this disputed in the case of the water moccasin, but remain skeptical.) In the case of the even-tempered and beautiful coral snake, you might practically have to stick your finger in its mouth to be bitten. Children have been known to play with coral snakes for days, without getting so much as a scratch. (On the other hand, one hastens to add, coral snakes, like most people, *will* bite if stepped on, or choked, whatever their metaphysics.) The best bet for exploring in the Thicket is therefore a set of good, thick hiking boots: and the calm realization that thousands of people have hiked, fished, and hunted the area for years without being bitten, or even rattled at.

For every species of poisonous snake in the area there are five or six nonpoisonous species. Some of these, like the worm snake, the Louisiana pine snake and the red-bellied snake, are rare. It is quite possible that more rare species will be found. In the meantime even the most common species need to be protected. There are more varieties of snakes in the Big Thicket than in any region of comparable size in the United States. With the possible exception of Florida no *state* contains as many kinds of snakes as the seven or eight counties of the Thicket. Among the snakes you will find in the Big Thicket are: spreading adder, indigo snake, blind snake, coach whip, diamondback water snake, Girard's water snake, water pilot, sand snake, Texas rat snake, Hallowell's water snake, speckled king snake, DeKay's snake, horn snake, chicken snake, blue racer, bull snake, and scarlet king snake. Projections indicate that by the year 2010 over seven billion will inhabit the surface of this planet. Where will herpetologists go for their specimens if, in the meantime, places like the Thicket are allowed to be extinguished?

Most accounts of the sprawling wilderness are quick to point out that it contains four of this continent's five varieties of insect-eating plants. Only the venus fly-trap is missing; the pitcher plant, bladderwort, sundew and bog violet grow there abundantly—

though less and less so, as bulldozers and brush hogs wreak havoc and swamps are drained. The number and the abundance of wildflowers in the Thicket are, to my way of thinking, far more impressive than the existence there of meat-eating plants. In her *I'll Take Texas*, Mary Lasswell describes a color slide show of the flowers of the Big Thicket. Her note pad, she laments, gave out at six hundred names:

> The list reads like the perennial section of the finest garden catalogue ever printed. . . . I sat there in complete disbelief at what I saw: *Lobelia cardinalis* five feet high; bergamot, cream and gold. Bluebells . . . *Lilium canadense*, wild petunia, Drummond phlox, winecups; coral bean; giant trumpet vine; wild wisteria; pentstemon, a climbing form rare in most other parts of the world. Wild honeysuckle and verbena. Great blankets of gaillardia and blazing star, spider lily, yellow fringed orchid, and tway-blade, and white fragrant orchid. These are but a scant handfull of the beauty native to the Thicket.

Miss Lasswell's enthusiasm is not misplaced. Lance Rosier, a self-trained biologist who lived in the Thicket all of his life, once remarked that he had once counted over eighty-four varieties of wildflowers in one morning in a single bend in the road near the Hardin County Consolidated School; he added that there was no use in going back next spring to see them—the place had subsequently been bulldozed. There are, Rosier speculated, over 1,000 varieties of flowering plants in the Big Thicket, if one includes flowering vines, trees, and shrubs. Not all of these could have been bulldozed into oblivion, even were there some massive, secret plot to do so. Some of the region's flowers are rare and unusually interesting. Among these are the pennywort, the bottle gentian, and a species of bartonia, as well as grass-of-parnassus and the granite gooseberry, in the saxifrage family. One need not be a trained botanist, however, to appreciate the beauty of the bluebonnet, Carolina lily, redbud, oleander, verbena, phlox, morning glory, Indian pink, blue larkspur sunflower, and hundreds of other flowers that grow wild, in the lush profusion, on the roadsides, pastures and pond margins of the Thicket.

The list of Thicket wildflowers, incidentally, is by no means complete. As this book goes to press three flowers on display at the Big Thicket Museum in Saratoga remain to be identified though several trained botanists have had a crack at them. This last spring Geraldine Watson discovered ten previously unnoticed species of flowers growing on sandy hill soils of the Upper Thicket. The flowers came as a big surprise to knowledgeable botanists, for they turned out to be desert species. No one had thought that they even existed in East Texas until they were discovered in the Big Thicket. Equally surprising were three species of flowers (a wahlinburgia, a species of hibiscus, and a species of bladderwort) never before collected in Texas, whose range lies in the eastern United States, and a species of sedge not previously known to exist south of northern Missouri.

By the time—hopefully not too distant—that Geraldine Watson and Peggy Amerson publish their long-awaited book on the wildflowers of the Big Thicket, it is entirely probable that more surprising plant specimens will have been uncovered.

By far the most puzzling case of anomalous distribution which I have run across is the claim made in the 1930's by a biologist who had engaged in the original biological survey to have found three plants in the Big Thicket whose only other known occurrence at that time was in Iceland. The biologist is now long deceased, and efforts to discover which plants he referred to have been futile. It is possible that the claim is valid, but until someone can come up with definite evidence one can only file the puzzle under the "unsolved" heading. The ecological ties between Iceland and the Big Thicket certainly seem tenuous enough. On the other hand, one never knows about the Thicket.

Though some flowers are found blooming in the region in every month of the year, the spring months produce an abundant crop. In the deep woods dogwood and magnolia burst suddenly into flower. Wild azalea and redbud and wild orchids appear overnight, spangling the new green of April grass and trees with blazing colors: pink, white, red, yellow. Ferns unfurl in deep creekbottoms, honeysuckle begins its creep along fencelines and saplings. Colored toadstools fleck the dull forest floor.

It usually comes as a shock to most people to hear that the Thicket's spring carpet of flowers contains orchids. It should come as even more of a surprise to learn that there are so many kinds of orchids there: at least thirty species, estimating conservatively. Not all are as large and as striking as the plants in a florist shop; but many are a great deal rarer. Among the orchids of the area are the shadowwitch (Ponthieu's orchid), crested coral root, southern twayblade, snakemouth, spreading pogonia, lace-lip spiral orchid, snowy orchid, giant spiral orchid, giant ladies tresses and water spider orchid. Sharing the orchids' damp, boggy habitat are a large number of orchid relatives and some thirty varieties of ferns. The Thicket hiker is very likely to find cinnamon fern, sensitive fern, southern lady-fern, water fern, woodsia and Christmas fern on shaded creekbanks and under thicket-tangle. In the spring and summer he will pause to examine tree trunks and branches thick with moss and resurrection fern. And, if he is fortunate, he may discover a species of fern no one had previously thought could exist in the region, as happened recently with the discovery of Florida shieldfern, in the Neches River lowlands.

While birds, wildflowers, and ferns have a natural grace and beauty that attracts us, the same cannot be said for the last item on this inventory, the molds and fungi. To date the molds and fungi of the Big Thicket have scarcely begun to be investigated; it is estimated that from one to two thousand species common to the region remain to be classified and studied. This little bit of information may not sound like big news, but the fact remains that a mold was the source of penicillin. And it may well turn out that a mold or fungus will be the source of a cure for cancer, or encephalitis, or muscular dystrophy. One thing is certain. Bulldozing, brush-hogging and tree-spraying can destroy the habitat of fungi as easily as of a rare bird or an unusual orchid. In our heedless rush to decapitate nature, even the humblest and least beautiful of things need our protection.

Catalogues and inventories are at best efficient; at worst they are dull. No minister ever preached the entire Old Testament series of "begats." No one since the Greeks has been able to endure Homer's entire catalogue of ships. Walt Whitman's catalogue of sights, smells, sounds at first produces verisimilitude, then tedium, and then an uncontrollable desire to read Emily Dickinson or Ernest Hemingway. The present catalogue of *flora* and *fauna*, therefore, must call for some apology. Though it is the only way, in a short space, to give a realistic picture of what is in the Thicket, it is misleading. In an inventory all items are carefully grouped together and numbered; in the Thicket plants, birds, reptiles, mammals are mixed up together in shifting, changing, unnumbered patterns. In an inventory everything is orderly and predictable; in the Thicket things are surprising; you never know what you will find around the next bend. An inventory, as a cold fact, is boring; the Thicket is never so.

It is possible, however, to correct the picture left by catalogues and inventories. One must put things back into their "natural" place and view them as a whole. One way of doing this is through the science of ecology: i.e., by viewing living things as systems or communities in which each element is dependent upon every other. Such an approach will be pursued in the next chapter. A second way of achieving the same goal is by describing the region through one's personal acquaintance with it. To me, this approach gives the profoundest sense of reality, though, apart from ecological insight, it is liable to go astray. What follows is a brief set of notes taken on a day's hike up Pine Island Bayou, in the heart of the traditional Thicket. The trek was made in July—not an ideal time for hiking. And, to complicate things, for a long while the writer was lost, or thought he was. The general impression was that of being cast out into a jungle, in which nature, and not man, held all the trumps. The experience, the writer thought, was a valuable one.

In the Thicket, moods change imperceptibly. The bayou meanders endlessly between low-leaf-matted banks, the sun filters down through tall cypress and hickory. The bayou water is coffee brown and, in the blaze of sunlight, faintly green. A fish darts into the green light and disappears; a turtle submerges suddenly off a rotting log. A mile from the road there is woods-silence; insects chirr, frogs chorus, an owl mutters sleepily at noon: but you can hear no car, no human voice, or door slamming—not even a dog. Wild hogs crash heavily through thick brush, rattling palmetto palms; a big woodpecker drums somewhere on a dead tree; leaves fall from the high branches, rattling on the forest floor.

From noon until sundown you walk and never see a house, or shed, or tilled field. There is one lumber company road, crossing the bayou, and two places where the bayou is bisected by pipeline. The pipeline lane is empty, far as the eye can see. Buzzards circle the pinetops; grass shimmers in afternoon heat. In the distance, cattle graze: the pipeline corridor disappears in far-off hazy woods. Then, on the other side of the brief corridor, the woods close over again. A water moccasin sprawls on a mossed bank, dropping heavily into murky water; an egret bursts up suddenly from among tall cypress knees and flies out of sight among beech and cypress, squawking; an animal, perhaps a fox, flees back into the woods so silently and quickly that it is only a moving shadow among grass and hanging vines.

Late in the afternoon the sunlight lengthens. Along the banks there are wildcat tracks, coming down off higher ground. The owls are calling to each other from deepening shadows. The mood has changed. Yellow light streaks the palmetto palms, touching the bayou water and the trunks of big cypresses. You should have reached the road by now. The labyrinth of bayou, swamp, vines has led you astray somewhere. You stop and check a compass and the sun's slant. In the flat, heavy noon distances faded, sameness reigned. Now the woods are murky, you can peer back into hidden depths. Back in the woods-cover an animal breaks a branch, a vine quivers. The owls mutter to each other solemnly. It is time to head out of the Thicket, following a game trail, and then two tire tracks toward the west sun. It takes two hours to walk to the highway; from there it is four miles to a settlement. Up in the pinetops, above the road, a wind is blowing, a hawk circles and dives. It is the first time you have noticed the wind since noon, when you stepped into the woods. It feels strange to hear a car finally coming down the highway. Everything feels different, in the new light of dusk.

3

ecology
the thicket as a whole

Not everyone finds the diversity, complexity and biological richness of the Big Thicket fascinating. For some people the region's very diversity constitutes a stumbling block. If you cannot tell me in one simple sentence just what the Thicket is, they ask, how can you expect me to evaluate it? If you cannot even tell me precisely *where* it is, they add, how can you ask me to "save" it? Such questions are understandable. No two maps of the Thicket follow exactly the same boundary lines; and if all the articles and books written about it were laid end to end, they certainly would not reach an agreement. This uncertainty does present the conservationist with a clear obligation. In one way or another he must give a clear account of where the Big Thicket is; and he must attempt, with some degree of accuracy, to say *what* it is. Otherwise he would be in the position of recommending the creation of a national park without being able to say where it should be located or what it would contain.

The conservationist is not dismayed by controversies surrounding the Big Thicket, or by its indefiniteness as a region. The Thicket is not a geographic feature like a river or a mountain. It is an ecological entity, and such entities rarely have precise boundaries. In this instance, uncertainties are not a stumbling block but an occasion for rejoicing, for they demonstrate the region's extreme variety and biological richness. And it is precisely this variety and richness which constitutes the strongest argument for its preservation.

The Big Thicket has been located differently at different times. In spite of disagreements over points of detail, however, there is considerable agreement concerning the region's general location. To the pioneers, "Big Thicket":

> . . . was the name originally applied to the area between the old San Antonio Road and the coastal prairie of South Texas from the Sabine River

43

on the east as far west as the Brazos River. . . . As settlement progressed, it became evident that the impenetrable thickets stopped far short of the Brazos, and the Trinity River came to be considered their western border. (*The Handbook of Texas*, 1952)

The only real exception to this general picture is offered by J. Frank Dobie, who describes the region as extending for 140 miles north and south along the Sabine River (boundary between Louisiana and Texas) and having a greatest width of fifty miles. How Dobie managed to place the Thicket in such an awkward position is hard to say. Since no one else has placed it there, however, we are justified in locating it in its traditional place and never allowing it again, as Dobie does, to try to escape into Louisiana. The *Biological Survey of the East Texas Big Thicket Area* (1938) contains a map of the original wilderness which conforms strongly to the description given by the early settlers. The Original Thicket, as claimed in the *Biological Survey*, took in all or part of fourteen counties and comprised 3,350,000 acres: an area (5,234 square miles) roughly the size of the State of Connecticut (5,009 square miles) or one-half the size of Maryland (10,577 square miles), which began just north of Beaumont, sprawled west almost to the Brazos River in Grimes County and extended northeast just south of Lufkin to the Louisiana state line. (See map, Figure 1.) By the 1930's only a small portion of this original area still bore the name or appearance of the Thicket.

A more recent map of the Big Thicket was proposed in 1967 by Professor Claude A. McLeod of Sam Houston State University in Huntsville, Texas. Professor McLeod's map is based on a careful ecological survey and must be taken seriously by anyone attempting to understand the nature and extent of the Thicket region. According to McLeod the Big Thicket stretches from the Louisiana border westward into Montgomery County near Conroe. (See map, Figure 1.) Unlike the earlier *Biological Survey*, however, he excludes parts of Walker, Trinity, San Augustine and Grimes counties from the Big Thicket proper. It is interesting to note that McLeod includes the northeastern tip of Harris County in the original Thicket, thereby bringing the southwestern limits of the region almost as near to Houston as its southeastern limits are to Beaumont.

The biological identity of the Big Thicket, according to McLeod, cannot be doubted. Its forest type:

> . . . is sufficiently homogeneous in species composition to delineate it from adjacent vegetational types. Likewise the vegetational structure holds in both dominant and understory indicator species through the entire area, thus sustaining both in concept and definition The Big Thicket of East Texas.

Ecologically, he goes on to add,

44

. . . the Big Thicket vegetation may be briefly defined as an edaphic-mesophytic climax forest type, predominantly a loblolly pine-hardwood association, abounding in a rich understory of both evergreen and deciduous shrubs, a variety of climbing vines, and both annual and perennial herbs.

This "brief" definition needs a little explaining. By "edaphic" is meant, simply, a specific type of soil. By "mesophytic" is meant plant species which exist under conditions of medium rainfall and temperature. In defining the area as a "loblolly pine-hardwood association" McLeod wishes to make it clear that, from the viewpoint of its vegetation, the Big Thicket must be understood as a region in which the moisture-loving loblolly pine is found together in conjunction with a specific set of hardwood trees: southern magnolia, beech, white-oak and, in some places swamp chestnut oak. Wherever in Southeast Texas you run across magnolias growing together with loblolly pines, you are pretty sure to have found a stand of the original Big Thicket vegetation.

If this unique type of pine-hardwood forest is what distinguishes the Big Thicket from surrounding prairies and piney woods, it is at the same time what stamps it as an extension of the Southern woodlands generally. The Southern Evergreen Forest sweeps westward from Virginia through Mississippi and southeastern Missouri into East Texas. Its southwesternmost extension is reached west of Conroe, Texas; its southernmost limits are in central Florida. The mixture of eastern and western plants in the Big Thicket is explained by its position at the western extreme of the evergreen forest. Its southern exposure guarantees it abundant rainfall and subtropical climate, which in turn make possible its mixture of tropical and temperate species. Its soil conditions, in turn, explain why the Thicket should contain such an *intensification* of the evergreen forest just before its disappearance at the edge of the post oak country and the blackland prairies to the west. In brief: geographical location explains the Big Thicket's diversity; rich, water-bearing soils explain both its botanical lushness and its pine-magnolia ecology; its dominant species stamp it as an outgrowth of the Southern forests generally—the last outgrowth, and the most interesting.

The earlier *Biological Survey* (1938) had defined the Big Thicket as a "temperate zone mezophytic jungle." As McLeod points out, this definition is misleading as it stands. Much of the original Thicket must have been a deeply shaded woodland largely free of dense growths of vines, grasses and shrubs. It must have been an open woods, relatively easy to travel, and more like the Indians' Big Woods than the pioneers' Big Thicket. At the same time, the Thicket has, and always has had, its jungle areas. The pioneers' picture of the Big Thicket as indeed a *thicket* cannot have been entirely false. It is certainly true that some of the present jungle-like areas in the Thicket have been produced, as Professor McLeod holds, by cutting down the "overstory" of big trees. The full sunlight then reaches down to vines, shrubs, and small trees which respond to their new situation with

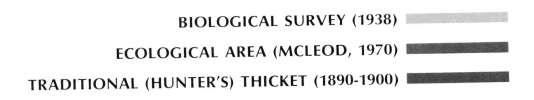

BIOLOGICAL SURVEY (1938)

ECOLOGICAL AREA (MCLEOD, 1970)

TRADITIONAL (HUNTER'S) THICKET (1890-1900)

Figure 1. Transposition of three maps of The Big Thicket: Biological Survey, McLeod's Ecological Analysis, and the Traditional Thicket.

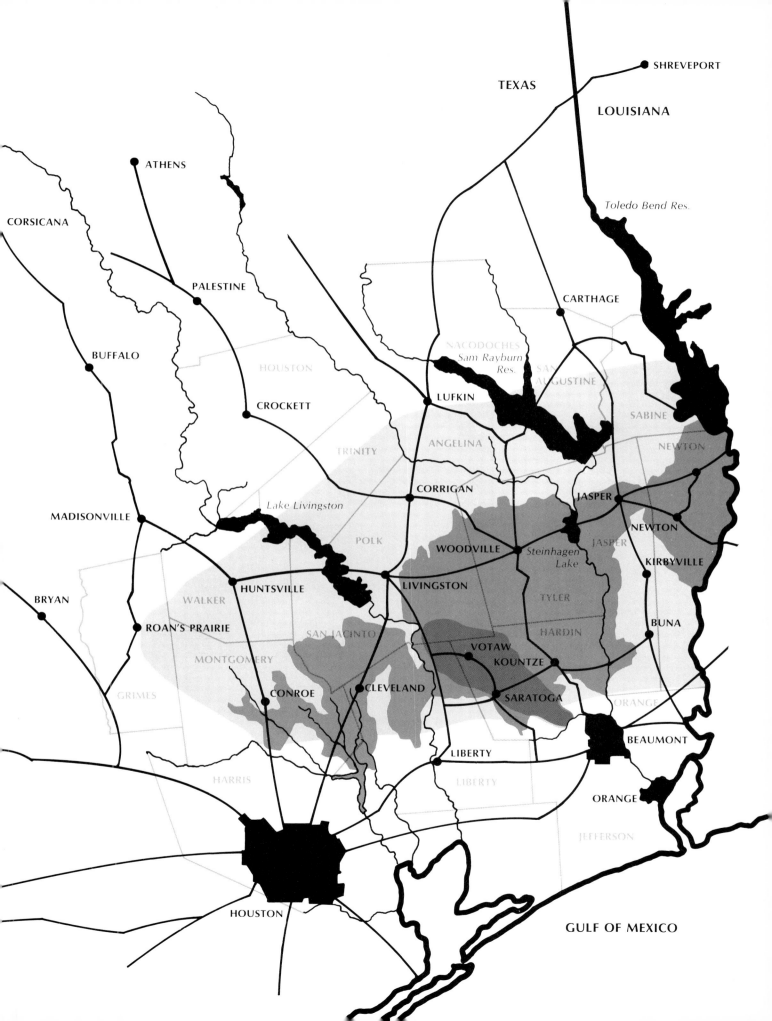

TEXAS

LOUISIANA

SHREVEPORT

Toledo Bend Res.

CORSICANA

ATHENS

PALESTINE

CARTHAGE

BUFFALO

HOUSTON

NACODOCHES

Sam Rayburn
Res.

SAN
AUGUSTINE

CROCKETT

LUFKIN

ANGELINA

SABINE

NEWTON

TRINITY

CORRIGAN

JASPER

MADISONVILLE

Lake Livingston

POLK

WOODVILLE

Steinhagen
Lake

NEWTON

JASPER

KIRBYVILLE

BRYAN

WALKER

HUNTSVILLE

LIVINGSTON

TYLER

BUNA

ROAN'S PRAIRIE

SAN JACINTO

HARDIN

MONTGOMERY

VOTAW
KOUNTZE

GRIMES

CONROE

CLEVELAND

SARATOGA

ORANGE

LIBERTY

BEAUMONT

HARRIS

LIBERTY

ORANGE

JEFFERSON

HOUSTON

GULF OF MEXICO

riotous growth. All such dense areas could not have been produced in this way, however. One of the earliest accounts of the Thicket is recorded in the journal of Gideon Lincecum, a doctor who came to Texas in the 1830's from Mississippi. On February 9, 1835, Lincecum wrote of crossing Big Alabama Creek. On the next day he noted:

> This day passed through the thickest woods I ever saw. It perhaps surpasses any country in the world for brush. There are 8 or 10 kinds of green undergrowth, privy, holly, 3 or 4 sorts of bay, wild peach trees, bayberry, etc., and so thick you could not see a man 20 yards for miles. The soil is pretty good and the water the very best. . . .

This was long before anyone had thought of timbering the Big Thicket, even on a modest scale. One must conclude from Lincecum's testimony that certain extensive parts of the region have always been "thicket," and not open woods. Doubtless both conditions existed there from the beginning, just as both exist there, though in far different proportions, today. Professor Donovan Correll of the Texas Research Foundation points out that large areas of the present Big Thicket closely resemble the jungles of Mexico in which he has done field work. The matter is predictably complex. The Big Thicket was not and is not a gigantic jungle. Yet it is one of the two places in North America extensive parts of which can lay claim to being jungle country. The other is the southmost tip of the Florida Everglades.

This picture of complexity is further strengthened by the appearance of broad ecological subdivisions within the overall region. There are, McLeod holds, three distinct subregions in the Thicket: the Upper Thicket, the Lower Thicket, and the Stream Thicket. The Upper Thicket is "dominated in its climax form" by a mixture of loblolly pine, white oak, beech and magnolia. ("Climax form" means, to an ecologist, the form achieved by a mature, long-standing forest.) It is better drained and more hilly than the Lower Thicket. It is particularly open country, a case of the "Big Woods" rather than the stereotyped "Big Thicket." The Lower Thicket is flatter and swampier than the Upper Thicket. It has no beech trees; the swamp chestnut oak takes its place. Farther to the east, in Newton and Jasper counties lies the Stream Thicket, marked by the presence of typical Thicket plant communities along small, swift-running streams. McLeod's general map and his subregions have been attacked by both conservationists and lumber interests alike. Lumbermen complain that the Big Thicket does not now reach and never has reached as far southwest as McLeod would have it. Conservationists, as a rule, insist that the Thicket overflows McLeod's boundaries and takes in adjacent areas.

I have examined, with Professor McLeod, the terminus-point of the Thicket southwest of Conroe and seen there the same loblolly pine-magnolia-beech-swamp oak association that occurs above the Alabama and Coushatta Indian Reservation in Polk County and in Hardin County below Saratoga. There can be no question but that the Thicket

extends southwest to this point, so long as its basic ecology is defined as McLeod defines it.

There are those who wish to define the Big Thicket more broadly than McLeod, as an entire region of transition. They would point out that the lack of a single "indicator species" in a given area does not disqualify it as Big Thicket country. And they would add that further ecological boundaries might well emerge if other trees and shrubs than those McLeod uses were examined in terms of their geographical distribution. There are many areas both alongside and well beyond the borders of McLeod's Thicket that look suspiciously like the Big Thicket, though an "indicator species" may be missing. And one wonders what sorts of maps could be drawn for the distribution of titi (cyrilla), dwarf palmetto, maple, tupelo, elm, pecan, and several other species that might be mentioned. These ought all to be considered "transition region," theorists insist, before the Thicket's boundaries are closed and its subregions established.

Not all conservationists share either McLeod's views or the idea that the Big Thicket is a vast "region of transition." Some accept the traditional notions of the turn-of-the-century hunter and trapper as definitive:

> To East Texas sportsmen of 1900 the Big Thicket meant northwestern
> Hardin and southeastern Polk counties. It was, and by many continues to
> be, considered to extend eastward. . . . (*The Handbook of Texas*, 1952)

This particularly dense, wild area along Little and Big Pine Island bayous was widely known as one of the last refuges of bear and panther in the Thicket and as a particularly good hunting ground for other kinds of game as well. Maps of this subregion, which I will term the "Traditional Thicket," have been published by Francis E. Abernethy and Archer Fullingim. (See Figure 1.) When viewed in the light of Professor McLeod's analysis, the traditional Thicket turns out to be a small subregion in the Lower Thicket. It excludes not only most of the Upper and all of the Stream Thicket, but more than half of the Lower Thicket as well. Needless to say, it also excludes any reference to "regions of transition": or to any region beyond the junctures of Polk, Hardin, and Liberty counties. Archer Fullingim and many others have argued long and well for the preservation of this area, with its dense undergrowth, rich historical associations, and its still largely undemolished wilderness character. There is much merit in their arguments. But the Hunter's Thicket, though it may be said to comprise a distinct subregion, is only that. (See map, Figure 1.) It is not the whole Big Thicket. It may indeed, if one wishes, be called the "heart" of the "Traditional Big Thicket"; but the Big Thicket has legs, arms, and a body as well, extending far beyond this traditional heart. Much more than this traditional area must be saved if justice is to be done to the Big Thicket as a whole.

The problem of locating the Big Thicket is bound up closely with the problem of explaining how it came to exist in the first place. The most concerted attempt to explain

the genesis of the region was made in the 1930's and '40's by H. B. Parks, one of the leaders of the original biological survey. According to Parks the area's distinctive qualities are due to its having been, in recent geological times, the bottom of an inland sea. The present Big Thicket is a "fossil seabottom." Its low hills are ancient sand dunes; its level stretches are old sandflats and beach margins; its swamp and bogs are prehistoric lagoons, or ponds created as dunes trapped retreating seas. Wind, water, and sand—and countless millennia—labored unknowingly to create it.

At the end of the Weches Time (Mount Selman), Parks explained, a new shoreline was created running southwest across the present State of Texas from just south of old Sabinetown to the Nueces River and possibly south to the Rio Grande. This shoreline included a large bay extending almost to the present towns of Nacogdoches and Huntsville and including portions of Louisiana.

> With the coming of the Pleistocene Age . . . the transgression and regression of the Gulf's water carried in sands from the depths of the Gulf and brought back sands of the Carrizo, Queen City and Sparta Ages, depositing them in this great, flat area.

Though to the casual observer it is not obvious, the topography of the region has every charcteristic of underwater deposits. Low sandbars and shoals which mark a receding seashore are present in abundance:

> These sand spits, dunes, and beach lines are now tied down with a wealth of vegetable cover seldom found outside the rain forests of the tropics.

The only places in the region which were originally bare were small lakes and salty meadows (savannahs) between sand dunes. The original soil was necessarily laid down in irregular patterns, in some places extending many miles beyond the floor of the original bay or inland sea along low valleys. This "fingering" of boundary lines is still another reason, beyond those created by legend and hearsay, why the Big Thicket should be so difficult to map.

Broadly speaking, two different bands of soil may be found underlying the region. The most recent, the Lissie sands, were laid down during the Pleistocene; they are poorly drained and have a relatively high acid content. The Pleistocene soils halt at a rather abrupt line of low hills just south of Livingston and Woodville, where the better drained, less acid soils of the Miocene Era (the Willis sands) begin. (Professor McLeod, incidentally, draws the boundary between the "Upper" and the "Lower" Big Thicket along the confluence of these two soil types.) Still further inland is an even older bank of soils marking the northern boundary of the Big Thicket region. All of the soil types typical of the Thicket are exceptionally capable of absorbing and holding water. The Big Thicket ends where its water-bearing soils end, at the edge of the farthest intrusions of the Gulf of

Mexico during the Pleistocene.

This picture of the Thicket as the former floor of an inland sea or bay having two distinct soil types seems refreshingly simple. Unfortunately, this simplicity is misleading. Throughout the region "foreign" soil types are patchworked in among the Thicket's basic soils, so that the overall result is a wide plurality of soil conditions—some similar to those along the coastal plains to the south, others similar to soils found to the west, north, and northeast. Once again, generalities must be tempered by an admission of many-sidedness. Dr. C. L. Lundell of the Texas Research Foundation points out that the Big Thicket has more varieties of soils than any area of comparable size in the United States. Hardin County alone has over one hundred soil types. The soils of the wilderness are varied enough to support the extreme variety of plant communities which inhabit it.

Parks' theory of the origin of the Big Thicket was capable of explaining not only its "fossil seafloor" topography and different soil types but the differing origins of its many plant species. As the water retreated in the original inland bay, Parks held, it left behind the seeds and shoots of vegetation swept down from the west by the ancestors of present-day rivers. Meanwhile the vast floodings of the Mississippi River during the Pleistocene brought in species from the northeast and east—some, possibly, from as far away as the mountains of Tennessee and Kentucky. Finally, the warm Gulf waters deposited their share of plants from the tropical south, plants which have thrived in exile. Professor D. S. Correll of the Texas Research Foundation points out that many of the local wild flowers are Appalachian in origin; when one maps their distribution it becomes evident that they occur in a direct line from Tennessee to the Thicket. As each species reaches the western extreme of its range in East Texas, it tends to differ from its eastern relatives. "The variations are often so great," Dr. Correll points out, "that the plant has to be segregated as a distinct species." The precise status of the Big Thicket as a "region of critical speciation" has yet to be worked out in detail, and constitutes one of the interesting puzzles surrounding the region. Another interesting puzzle is the occurrence within the Thicket of plant growth patterns found in the Appalachian mountains, but not between it and those mountains, hundreds of miles to the northeast. Biologists have yet to study the area's micro-ecology; its macro-ecology is incompletely studied, just as its bird and animal life have never been fully classified.

To the ecologist the variety of the area is as interesting, and as unique, as its variety of species and speciations is to the taxonomist. While it is the task of the taxonomist to classify living things in terms of their similarities and dissimilarities, the ecologist studies the dependence of organisms both on each other and on their physical environment. Plants and animals exist not as rugged individuals, but in communities. So delicate is the balance in many plant-and-animal communities that the disappearance or enfeebled function of one species may cause the disappearance of many others and force radical changes in the environment. Fortunately the wide variety of Thicket plants and animals has helped to stabilize and protect its ecology. Where one plant or animal has been rooted out, others have been able to step in to take its place.

Eight distinct plant communities exist within the confines of the Big Thicket: upland communities, savannahs, beech-magnolia communities, baygalls, palmetto-bald-cypress-hardwood communities, bogs, streambank communities, and floodplain forests. If one adds to this list the plants of the various natural prairies found there, the total number of plant communities comes to nine. A slightly different ecological analysis of the Thicket's plant communities will be suggested by Geraldine Watson in her forthcoming book on the wildflowers of the Big Thicket. Lumping together the acid bogs and baygalls as a single basic community, Watson arrives at a grand total of eight essential plant associations for the area: beech-magnolia-loblolly pine communities, upland pine savannahs, wetland savannahs, palmetto-hardwood flats, streambottom-hardwood associations, arid-sandyland communities, prairies, and swamplike communities (acid bogs and baygalls).

There is a great deal to be said for Watson's analysis. Interestingly, it adds to the basic types of Thicket *flora* an entirely different sort of association, the sandyland community, making the region's little understood connections with the arid west more apparent. In what follows, however, the earlier classification, followed in the 1967 National Park Service study of the Big Thicket, will be used. Needless to say, the existence of two contrasting taxonomic schemes to describe the plant communities of the area is taken not as some sort of liability, but as one more proof of its potential for scientific research and its exuberant botanical variety.

Between these widely varied associations there exists almost every conceivable sort of gradation. The National Park Service study of 1967 concludes:

> The forest contains elements common to the Florida Everglades, the
> Okefenokee Swamp, the Appalachian region, the piedmont forests, and
> the large open woodlands of the coastal plains. Some large areas resemble
> tropical jungles in the Mexican states of Tamaulipas and Vera Cruz.

Every plant community known to exist throughout the entire range of the Southern Evergreen Forest can be found in the Big Thicket. It is the only segment of the Southern Evergreen Forest, moreover, of which this can be said. Those who belittle the Big Thicket—and they are fewer and fewer—utterly fail to understand this point. You would search without success to find such a mingling of species and communities anywhere else on this continent. In this the Big Thicket is unique. It is North America's best-equipped ecological laboratory.

But ecological diversity can, as has already been noted, provide the conservationist with serious quandaries. The Big Thicket is no longer a single contiguous wilderness, and can therefore not be preserved simply by being set aside as a single all-encompassing park.

As late as 1938 biologists could claim that the region contained over a million acres untouched by axe or plow. Now the Thicket is generally conceded to contain 350,000 acres and to be shrinking at the rate of around fifty acres a day. Conservationists, faced with these hard facts, ask for a park encompassing from 100,00 to 200,000 acres. Lumber companies reply that a Big Thicket National Monument totalling from 35,000 to at the most 45,000 acres would protect all of the remaining biologically valuable land in the region. Not everyone agrees with the concept of a national monument. Ecologists insist angrily that the Big Thicket cannot be saved in isolated bits and pieces: unless it can be safeguarded as a whole, its individual parts will not continue to exist. You either save a lot of the Thicket, they argue, or you lose it all. "And what," they conclude, "is a Monument? It is something dead."

Even those who want to save the greater part of the remaining Thicket, however, agree with one of the principles underlying the concept of an area National Monument; namely, that certain ecological segments of the wilderness should be set aside for special protection and that these segments must contain specimens of every sort of habitat unique to the locale. Sizeable portions of each of the region's ecologies should be preserved unchanged, inviolate. The problem remains: Which portions? And what size?

One answer to these questions is found in the concept of a Thicket "String of Pearls": a proposal incorporated into the lumbermen's projected National Monument. In succeeding chapters the struggle to conserve the Big Thicket and the controversies surrounding various conservationist proposals will be described at length, revealing the tragic flaws (and, in part, the tragic destiny) of the Pearls. But before dealing with these flaws, it will be useful to give a brief account of the Pearls: their size, their character, their value. In this way the ecological diversity of the Big Thicket will be made strikingly evident.

In all, the total acreage of the String of Pearls adds up to 35,500 widely separated acres. Originally the National Park Service suggested that the following nine areas be preserved:

1. Big Thicket Profile	....	18,180 acres
2. Beech Creek	....	6,100 acres
3. Neches Bottom	....	3,040 acres
4. Tanner Bayou	....	4,800 acres
5. Hickory Creek Savannah	....	220 acres
6. Beaumont Unit	....	1,700 acres
7. Little Cypress Creek	....	860 acres
8. Loblolly	....	550 acres
9. Clear Fork Bog	....	50 acres

The Loblolly Unit (which has escaped timbering only because it has been entangled in

57

litigation since the turn of the century) contains the last extensive stand of virgin loblolly pines in East Texas.

The Clear Fork Bog Unit, though it consists of only fifty acres, is uniquely valuable. Sphagnum is a whitish-grey peat moss; in northern latitudes a sphagnum bog would be a peat bog. The Clear Fork Bog is a swamp tupelo-sphagnum association, which contains some surprising rare plants: a member of the gentian family which occurs nowhere else in the world, some tiny relatives of the orchids known to occur in only a few other places, several extremely rare members of the heath community, and the only examples of wild lily and wild trilium in Texas. Biologists call it a "botanical marvel." They are not exaggerating.

The Hickory Creek Savannah Unit is as different from the Clear Fork Bog as the African veldt is from the delta of the Nile. The word savannah has two uses. More generally, it connotes any tract of land covered with low vegetation: in short, a treeless plain or prairie. The second, more specific, meaning of the word is: any large area of tropical or subtropical grassland covered in part with trees and spiny shrubs. It is this second meaning which fits the Hickory Creek Savannah, which is a grassland expanse broken by occasional stately longleaf pines and a number of bushes, weeds, and low trees. The botanical value of this unit is twofold. First, the number of species of herbaceous plants which it contains runs into the hundreds; among these are many scarce species, including several orchids. Second, as a distinct forest type, it demonstrates graphically the influence of soil on vegetation. Like the longleaf pine country to the northeast, the Hickory Creek Savannah has relatively poor soils. Interestingly, the existence of this savannah appears also to be dependent on recurrent grass fires, which kill off intruding hardwoods and favor the growth of fire-resistant pines. It will be necessary periodically to burn parts of the Hickory Creek Savannah in order to preserve its ecology—paradoxical as that may seem. If it is not burned, hardwoods will take over and it will no longer be a savannah.

The Beaumont Unit, at the junction of Pine Island Bayou and the Neches River, is known historically as the Spears League. Though its position at the northern city limits of Beaumont places it just outside of the Big Thicket, it is a truly superlative representative of the Thicket's floodplain forest and streambank communities. A National Park Service study concluded that it is doubtful whether any finer stand of its basic hardwoods (baldcypress, water tupelo, river birch, american sycamore, american elm, overcup oak) exists anywhere else in North America. Quite possibly it is one of those rare places which have escaped timbering; certainly its sheltered position between two streams and its mazes of sloughs, ponds and cut-off riverbed have held back the bulldozer and the power saw in this century. Plans for preserving the Beaumont Unit include the purchase of a scenery-preserving strip of land along the south side of Pine Island Bayou within the Beaumont city limits and the east bank of the Neches River in Orange County. Access to the unit would be both by boat and by road; no "developments" would be placed there except pathways and possibly one or two footbridges.

The Beech Creek and Little Cypress Creek units are much alike, except that the Little Cypress Creek Unit is hillier and more deeply cut by streams. The deep, fertile soils of both areas support magnificent stands of the beech-magnolia-loblolly pine association which many scientists, following McLeod, insist is the symbol of the Big Thicket. Of particular interest is a small area on the west side of the Beech Creek Unit which apparently has never been cut. It is doubtful whether any finer expression of the original Thicket ecology can be found than in this "Woodland Chapel." The deeply shaded understory of this small area is open and leaf-matted, a condition which must once have been characteristic of a great deal of the Big Thicket but which is seldom found today. This grove thus can provide a sort of standard gauge according to which the regrowth of many of the areas under federal protection could be measured.

Though the Tanner Bayou Unit and the Neches Bottom Unit are located nearly fifty miles apart on two different rivers (the Trinity and the Neches, respectively), they exhibit closely similar terrain. Like the Beaumont Unit, both contain swamp and floodplain forest communities. The Neches Bottom Unit is laced with sloughs connected with the Neches River. The slightly elevated lands between the sloughs support immense specimens of birch, elm, oak, boxelder, and planertree; the sloughs contain majestic baldcypress and water tupelo. The Tanner Bayou Unit is one of the largest roadless tracts to be found in the Trinity River Bottomlands. It exhibits an interesting series of parallel "oxbow swales" marking the gradual shifts of the riverbed in the past. These and other parts of the unit contain standing water much of the year—a fact which may account for its having escaped destructive logging for so long. Conservationists point out that this unit has unusual importance as a bird rookery area. Great nesting colonies of herons, egrets, ibises, and roseate spoonbills use these bottomlands.

Larger than all the rest of the "pearls" put together and more diverse than any of them, the Big Thicket Profile Unit begins at the Alabama and Coushatta Indian Reservation on the highway from Livingston to Woodville and descends south into the "Lower Thicket," ending at the palmetto palm country southwest of Saratoga. Down its whole length this unit lies in some of the finest and most interesting sections of the Big Thicket forest. The Profile Unit takes in three important stream courses: Big Sandy Creek, Menard Creek, and Pine Island Bayou. As originally proposed, the unit was widened at three places to include especially interesting botanical areas.

About a mile below the Indian reservation the Profile Unit encounters the Big Sandy Creek drainage system and follows it for nearly seven miles. Just before leaving the creek, the unit is broadened into the first enlarged section, a wild, well-watered, relatively unaltered area containing a recognizable plurality of ecotypes, from upland communities to baygalls, bogs, streambank and floodplain (swamp) communities. This ecological diversity is reflected in the great variety of mammals, amphibians, birds, and reptiles—including alligators—which exist there. As the unit is continued south from the Big Sandy Creek section it crosses an interesting topographical feature, the divide between Big Sandy (which flows east into the Neches River) and Menard Creek, which, a little over a mile away, flows west into the Trinity River. It is unusual to find two such sizeable streams approaching each other so closely without "stream piracy" taking place.

South of this miniature "continental divide," the unit follows the Menard Creek Valley for five miles before veering slightly westward to take in part of the "Tight-Eye" region. There is some question concerning the term "Tight-Eye," which, like the word "baygall," is purely local in origin. It seems to refer to the exceptional density of the forest cover—its "tightness." At the same time, it could equally have arisen from the abundance of swamp cyrilla of "titi" bushes, which form impenetrable thickets in the area. The National Park Service reported in 1967 that the wilderness quality of the Tight-Eye

> . . . is probably unsurpassed in the Big Thicket, and the opportunities for experiencing such an environment by trail access and for trailside interpretation are outstanding. Also, the southern part of the tract contains the transition between the "upper" and "lower" components of the Big Thicket vegetative type, coinciding with a slight but abrupt change in topography as the relief becomes flatter.

Because of its location on a transition zone, or ecozone, this section of the Profile Unit was recommended as the location for the monument's central headquarters.

After leaving the Tight-Eye section, the Profile Unit heads southeast, following Pine Island Bayou for nearly twelve miles, ending in the palmetto-baldcypress-hardwood forest south of farm road 770, from Saratoga to Batson. It is the only part of the Profile Unit lying wholly within the "Traditional Big Thicket," and contains, to use the terminology of biologists, "fine examples of the baygall and streambank communities." It is a wild, nearly roadless, jungle-like country. Anyone who hikes there is sure of a wilderness experience: as the description at the end of the second chapter is intended to convey.

A convinced Big Thicket conservationist would, in spite of the variety and biological wealth of these "pearls," argue that they nonetheless constitute a very meager sample of the Big Thicket region. Is the rest of the Big Thicket to be sacrificed, and only those few pockets of wilderness retained? There are numerous stands of insect-eating plants (like, for example, the Hyatt's Estates Bog Preserves near Warren) which need protection. There are forests of wild cape jasmine and untold dozens of small plant communities (tupelo bogs, baygalls, sphagnum bogs) which are beginning to be studied just as the bulldozers are beginning to erase them. There are fern valleys of great beauty, and pre-Civil War cabins in secluded clearings that would make fascinating stopping places for

harried, urbanized Americans. There are heron rookeries back in the swamps, and free-flowing streams, and places like the recently discovered Sternberger tract which contains a medley of huge 300-year-old trees unlikely to be equalled anywhere between the Rockies and the Mississippi. There are places along Little Pine Island Bayou where cypress trees soar above the forest roof and cypress knees reach shoulder-high to a tall man. Should not these places too receive protection? Aren't they, just as much as any other areas, veritable "pearls"?

In the face of such objections as these, lumber, oil, and real estate interests have gone on about their business just as before—only with frighteningly greater efficiency. An example of this efficiency is the "soil shredder." Probably few of us have ever seen one. Lumber companies now use them on semicleared land to destroy not only all stumps, vines, grasses, and flowers above the ground but all root networks from three to four feet below the surface. The remains are then planted in endless rows of pulp pines—minus hardwoods, flowers, vines, brushes, ferns, and all the birds and wild animals that depend on a mixed ecology. In the wake of a soil shredder biological diversity is vanquished, sheer monotony reigns. But biological monotony is as dangerous as it is unaesthetic. When the complexity of an ecosystem is reduced, its ability to survive is diminished. A pine forest of a single species is a prime target for insect and bacterial diseases, which may strike suddenly and explosively. And when the pines are gone, what is left? The soil shredder. Over 30,000 acres of Big Thicket pine-hardwood forests *per year* are scheduled by the timber industry to be turned into pine plantations by this method. "If there're any birds in there," a biologist acquaintance of mine recently quipped of a pine plantation, "you can bet they're carrying knapsacks. There's nothing for them to eat." Nor do the copious insecticides sprayed on the rows of pines for insect protection improve the fishing in the streams which drain the pine plantations.

I do not mean to single out the soil shredder as if it were the only technological disaster confronting our woodlands. A bulldozer can accomplish almost the same feats as a soil shredder and almost as quickly. So can even simpler technologies. Recently lumber companies have sent men into the Big Thicket with orders to *girdle every hardwood tree on their lands.* This includes hardwoods in swamps, creekbeds, sloughs, lowlands of every description, where pine trees cannot ever grow. Conservationists question whether the motive for such policies can be simply the desire to produce more pulp pine.

The point of these remarks is simple enough. It is not only that the Big Thicket is now being timbered. Its richness, diversity, and uniqueness are now being totally obliterated: root and branch. It is not just that its trees are being cut. Its aesthetic qualities, its scientific values, are being cut to zero. Needlessly. And with, it appears to many, more than a little calculation. The Big Thicket exhibits a unique ecology, or rather, collection of ecosystems. It does not follow from this, however, that its ecology has been or will be respected. In the following two chapters a detailed account will be given both of attempts to respect and to destroy this ecology, and with it the uniqueness, value, and beauty of an entire region.

4

conservation
and anti·conservation

The idea of making the Big Thicket into a national park is not new. It dates back at least as far as 1927, when R. E. Jackson of Silsbee convened the first meeting of the East Texas Big Thicket Association. Jackson, a retired railroad conductor, had become interested in the region while working on trains that skirted its edges. He was to serve continuously as president of the association through its existence. Jackson's attempts at conservation were to be more than merely verbal and organizational. For many years he owned a lease of 22,000 acres of prime Big Thicket land at the southeast corner of Polk County: the "Tight-Eye" country, known for its botanical luxuriance and isolation. Jackson turned his lease into a game preserve and convened meetings of scientists, conservationists, and newspapermen there. Under the leadership of Jackson and others the campaign for the Big Thicket National Park slowly gained ground. By the mid-1930's proposals for preserving the area had been formulated and a number of prominent figures drawn into the organization.

In 1936 a biological survey of the region was undertaken under the supervision of Parks and Cory. Basing itself on this survey, the Texas Academy of Science closed its 1937 convention with a resolution calling for a concerted effort to secure "scientific protection" for the Big Thicket. By this time a number of political figures had allied themselves with the conservationists. Governor Allred, Congressman Martin Dies, and Senator Morris Sheppard all backed the proposed park. The Beaumont Chamber of Commerce seconded the positions taken by the political leaders, and articles on the Big Thicket began appearing in large Texas dailies.

It is interesting to read those articles today, from the sobering vantage point of 1971:

A total of 2,350,000 acres of wooded land, some of it overgrown so thickly with trees and brush that one has to cut his way through it, lies northwest of Beaumont a few miles. It is upon this veritable paradise for the nature lover, the hunter and other outdoorsmen that two mighty monsters, oil derricks and sawmills, are encroaching rapidly.... Officials of the East Texas Big Thicket Association and other organizations are working incessantly to have the entire forest purchased and preserved as a national or state park. Realizing the stupendous task that confronts them, the far-sighted members of the organization have an alternate plan and believe that it will ultimately be worked out. The association would preserve a tract of land of 430,000 acres which is bordered on the west by the Trinity River. This smaller tract, heavily wooded and containing the bigger portion of the palmetto land, which is so thickly overgrown that it is almost impenetrable, is approximately twenty-two miles in length north and south and twenty-one miles east and west. (*Dallas News*, 1937)

It is impossible to read these passages now without a twinge of despair. One attempts without success to imagine, in 1971, creating a "smaller" park containing a mere 430,000 acres. In that not so distant time there were few roads in the region, and those were mainly gravel, dirt, and tire track. No more than 15,000 people lived in the Thicket, and of these less than a thousand were estimated to live outside its scattered towns and hamlets. There were no vacation subdivisions; there were still substantial tracts of virgin timber; many oil field pipelines had not yet been bulldozed. No wonder a park of over 400,000 contiguous acres seemed a live possibility.

In November, 1938, Senator Sheppard ordered the National Park Service to investigate the Big Thicket for possible inclusion in the National Park System. A National Park Service investigation, led by acting regional director Herbert Maeir and wildlife technician W. B. McDougal, was concluded early in 1939. Basing itself on this survey, the National Park Service enthusiastically recommended the inclusion of the Big Thicket in the National Park System. Congressman Dies and Senator Sheppard immediately went to work to scrape up sufficient appropriations. To many, the Big Thicket National Park appeared to be almost a reality.

Yet it was not to be. The *Beaumont Enterprise* of February 2, 1939, juxtaposes two telling headlines:

ROOSEVELT 'ENEMY OF PEACE' NAZIS CRY. BERLIN PRESS HURLS TIRADE AGAINST PLAN TO AID FRANCE

BIG THICKET DISAPPEARANCE COMING UNLESS AREA MADE INTO A PARK SAYS R. E. JACKSON

The timber in the Thicket, Jackson explained, was being cut rapidly; within a generation or two there would be very little left. He appealed for aid from all those in favor of conservation to save a unique area that had received high praise both from the United States Biological Survey and the National Park Service. But Austria had already lost its independence; Czechoslovakia had ceased to exist; in seven months Hitler would invade Poland. Projects for conservation went by the board as plans for war multiplied. The Big Thicket was forgotten.

It was not soon to be remembered again. With the end of the Second World War interest was slow to focus again on problems of conservation. The East Texas Big Thicket Association continued to exist, a paper organization divided within itself and deeply eroded. An interview with Jackson in the January 2, 1955, *Houston Post* reveals the frustration and weariness of conservationists:

> Residents of Texas are standing idly by while one of the fabulous natural wonderlands in the nation is being destroyed. [says R. E. Jackson] Twenty-eight years ago he called a meeting of nature-lovers, scientists and botanists at his camp in the Thicket and the Big Thicket Association of which he has served continuously as president was formed. As president of the association, Jackson says he spent much of his own money making trips to Washington and to Austin where he pleaded with lawmakers to set up legislative measures to preserve the Thicket for posterity. Each time he tried to have something done, he was told both in Washington and Austin that there was no money for such a venture, he says. And now, after 28 years, he feels that the fight of his association is certainly doomed to failure. Roadways have been cut into the heart of the Thicket, timber is being cut and moved out, and wildlife is being ruthlessly destroyed, he says. Oil company crews are making exploration trips through the heart of the forest, and everywhere they go they are cutting down and killing out rare plants and trees.

A group of Houston nature lovers, Jackson added with bitter humor, had recently bought acreage on the fringes of the Thicket and were transplanting there shrubs, flowers, and trees expected to disappear in the rest of the region; they were calling themselves The Little Thicket Association.

It would be most unfortunate if the preceding brief account of the first efforts to create a Big Thicket National Park made it appear that the conservationist movement was the work of only one or two men. Many other names should be mentioned. Among them are Larry J. Fisher, whose photographs of the Big Thicket did more than many a speech to make the beauty of the region widely realized; Mrs. Ethel Osborne Hill, ninety-four years old, who even now continues to fight for the protection of the Thicket; Donald O. Baird, president of the Texas Academy of Science; Henry W. Flagg, president of the Texas Wildlife Federation; C. B. Marshall; Mrs. Bruce Reid; and many others.

If public forgetfulness can be long-lived, it nonetheless need not last forever. In

1961 two fortuitous events occurred. The first was the Department of the Interior's West Gulf Coastal Plain Type Study, which concluded that the Big Thicket should be given further attention as a possible addition to the National Park System. The second, which was given far more public exposure, was the decision of the then-reigning governor of Texas, Price Daniel, to make the Big Thicket a campaign issue in his bid for an unprecedented fourth term. Daniel's Big Thicket proposals were unique: the smallest park ever suggested (20,000 acres) was advertised alongside the largest map of the original wilderness ever drawn. The governor's concern over the Big Thicket was not superficial. He was raised in the area, and had long taken an interest in its conservation. Unfortunately, however, his proposals were taken as just another political gambit designed to get votes, and his subsequent defeat at the polls was accompanied by a newly aroused resentment at the idea of any Big Thicket Park, state or national, large or small. Public forgetfulness was followed by an era of public negation.

Forgetfulness might have reigned again, had not opponents of the park overreacted. The sudden appearance of a new drive to create a park in the region was accompanied by the equally sudden appearance of fantastic rumors, circulated by park opponents. Local people were told that millions of visitors would come in and take over their homes; that their children would be eaten by government-introduced bears and panthers; that all local schools would be closed; that there would be no more hunting and fishing whatsoever; and that old people would be kicked out of their homes and farms. The old bogey of economic disaster was dragged out and refurbished. The park, it was said, would drive the lumber industry out and destroy all jobs in the area. The loss of revenue from lands owned by "the Feds" and no longer taxable would drive small area towns into bankruptcy. No one seemed to heed the obvious argument that a park would bring in a new industry (tourism) to complement the old (lumbering). Of course, that would break the monolithic, almost feudal control of the lumber interests over the region—particularly over its company-owned towns.

It took a while, but opposition to the idea of a park finally created its counter-opposition. The East Texas Big Thicket Association had long ago died a faltering, pitiful death. On November 13, 1964, a new conservationist organization, the Big Thicket Association of Texas, was formed on the ruins of the old. For all its dedication and tenacity, the prior Thicket Association had been hampered by narrowly provincial viewpoints and lack of "connections." The new association was to act with far greater sophistication, and was consequently able to draw some prestigious and powerful men into its orbit. Its new president, Dempsie Henley, was well known through Southeast Texas and, what is more important, knew how to generate support from the "establishment"—and how to pry publicity out of the information media.

The first objective undertaken by the association—to persuade the State of Texas to take an interest in conservation—appeared an exercise in futility. The Lone Star State is dominated by interests which could care less about wilderness conservation, and the public mind is—or has been until recently—apathetic. Governor Daniel had created a statewide committee to study the Thicket as a possible park site; but it was not funded, and had only semiofficial status. Representatives of lumber companies were included on the committee; these, however, managed not to attend after the first meeting, doubtless reasoning that they could thereby hobble any effort to complete the committee's report. The lumbermen had little to fear. Their man, John Connally, was now governor. When Governor Conally finally did visit the Thicket, he came in an airplane chartered by Eastex, one of the biggest lumber companies in the area.

The committee report, however, was duly presented to the governor on March 24, 1965, and quickly forgotten by him, after a number of verbal flourishes. The committee made six recommendations. First, an additional 2,000 acres of land should be purchased for the Alabama and Coushatta Indian Reservation, which would become an integral part of the park. Second, immediately adjacent to the reservation a 200 acre camping area should be created. Third, a Big Thicket State Forest of 10,000 acres should be created to the south of the camping area. Hiking trails, riding paths, and swimming facilities should be included in the forest. Fourth, a 15,000 acre wildlife and wilderness area should be created in the country bounded by Saratoga, Sour Lake, and Daisetta, and should be restocked with the animals once plentiful in the region: bear, panther, turkey, deer. (Moose, javelina, buffalo, and English boar were also thrown in for good measure.) Fifth, a camp headquarters should be set up at Saratoga. Finally, the areas surrounding these five features should be subject to joint control by state government and private owners (with an accompanying tax break for the owners) to ensure game and lumber production for the foreseeable future.

It was not the first good idea to sink forgotten into the murky backwaters of Texas politics. But sink it did. The legislature and the governor remained indifferent. The lumber interests went their way in blissful peace. Perhaps, at last, the whole thing would be forgotten.

It might well have been forgotten were it not for the intervention of an entirely new force: the federal government, as represented by the Department of the Interior on the one hand and Senator Ralph Yarborough on the other. Raised in East Texas on the banks of the Neches River, not far north of the Big Thicket, the senator had long had an interest in the colorful region and its preservation. The only successful conservationist in Texas history, he was to lead the fight for the creation of the beautiful Padre Island National Seashore and the Guadalupe Mountains National Park. It was only a matter of time before his long-term interest in the Big Thicket would spill over into action.

Anyone wishing to read a full account of the senator's Big Thicket Tour in October, 1965, should consult Dempsie Henley's *The Murder of Silence*, where it is reported in detail. The tour included Clarence Cottam, director of the Welder Wildlife

Foundation; Dr. Donovan S. Correll of the Texas Research Foundation; Jim Bowmer, president of the Texas Explorers Club; Bill Bowen, superintendent of the Padre Island National Seashore; Dempsie Henley, president of the Big Thicket Association; and Lance Rosier, the patient self-taught naturalist whose reflections form the basis for the next chapter. In sum, the senator heard and took the advice of those who knew the Big Thicket best. They convinced him—assuming that he needed convincing—of the region's unique value and beauty. The end result was Senate Bill No. 3929 to create a Big Thicket National Park.

There is many a slip twixt the lip and the cup. There are many more slips, turns, and twists between the introduction of a legislative measure and its enactment into law—assuming that it is ever so enacted. Senator Yarborough's bill was read twice on October 20, 1966, and referred to the Committee on Interior and Insular Affairs, where it nestled cozily for nearly five years:

> *Be it enacted by the Senate and House of Representatives of the United States of America in Congress assembled,* That, in order to preserve in public ownership an area in the State of Texas possessing outstanding botanical and zoological values together with scenic and other natural values of great significance, the Secretary of the Interior shall establish the Big Thicket National Park, consisting of land and interests in land not in excess of seventy-five thousand acres in Hardin, Liberty, San Jacinto, Polk and Tyler Counties, Texas.
>
> Sec. 2. (a) To establish the Big Thicket National Park, the Secretary of the Interior may acquire land or interests therein by donation, purchase with donated or appropriated funds, exchange, or in such other manner as he deems it in the public interest. Wherever feasible, land shall be acquired by transfer from other Federal agencies.
>
> Any property, or interest therein, owned by the State of Texas or political subdivision thereof may be acquired only with the concurrence of such owner.
>
> (b) In order to facilitate the acquisition of privately owned lands in the park by exchange and avoid the payment of severance costs, the Secretary of the Interior may acquire land which lies adjacent to or in the vicinity of the park. Land so acquired outside the park boundary may be exchanged by the secretary on an equal-value basis, subject to such terms, conditions and reservations as he may deem necessary, for privately owned land located within the park. The Secretary may accept cash from or pay cash to the grantor in such exchange in order to equalize the values of the properties exchanged.
>
> Sec. 3. When title to all privately owned land within the boundary of the park, other than such outstanding interests, rights, and easements as the Secretary determines are not objectionable, is vested in the United States, notice therefore of and notice of the establishment of the Big

Thicket National Park shall be published in the Federal Register. Thereafter, the Secretary may continue to acquire the remaining land and interests in land within the boundaries of the park.

Sec. 4. The Big Thicket National Park shall be administered by the Secretary of the Interior in accordance with the provisions of the Act of August 25, 1916 (39 Stat. 535; 16 U.S.C. 1-4), as amended and supplemented.

Sec. 5. There are hereby authorized to be appropriated such funds as are necessary to accomplish the purpose of this Act.

Long-winded, you may say. And isn't the whole point made in the first paragraph anyhow? The answer is, Yes; but it is also, No. There is a lot more to creating a National Park than simply issuing a one paragraph proclamation. Landowners must be paid for the loss of increasingly hard-to-find land. Owners are often more adequately repaid through the substitution of comparable acreage for the land taken over by the government. In all transfers of purchases of land there are problems of survey, titles, leases, and unsettled local disputes. In the Big Thicket, overlapping oil, timber, and hunting leases combine with ill-surveyed boundaries and titles dating hazily back to Spanish land grants make the simple purchase of land a knotty problem. Finally, even were the bill to create a park passed and signed, a further separate bill authorizing appropriations would have to be dug out of committee, passed by Congress, and signed. No wonder it is such a long journey between the reading of a bill and the reality it is intended to create.

In November, 1965, the National Park Service had made a preliminary reconnaissance of the Thicket and arrived at a favorable conclusion. A second study was made in October, 1966, at the same time that Yarborough was preparing and reading his bill before the Senate; this study was sufficiently thorough to make possible some detailed recommendations. In general the National Park Service followed the ecological analysis of the region developed by Claude A. McLeod. An upper and a lower Thicket were mapped out, following McLeod, and representative "specimen areas" were selected for preservation. The result was the Big Thicket "String of Pearls" discussed in the last chapter: 35,000 acres of widely dispersed tracts connected with (hopefully) scenic roadways. Needless to say, lumber companies—who helped in the compilation of the 1966 study— were delighted with its conclusions.

Conservationists, however, have almost without exception disagreed emphatically with important aspects of the 1966 report. Its general conclusions are satisfactory enough. The realization that the Thicket contains its measure of plants not known elsewhere, as well as many not protected anywhere in the National Park System, the assertion that the region is ecologically both unique and unquestionably of national significance, are bound to gladden the heart of any conservationist. But, conservationists ask, what is the use of preserving small patches of pristine wilderness if they are going to be sur-

rounded in ten years with red flag subdivisions, filling stations, barbecue joints, Dairy Queens, and the rest of the suburban paraphernalia most tourists are trying to get away from? Will the "pearls" be beautiful then? Even worse, conservationists ask, how will these minute areas withstand the pressure of hundreds of thousands of tourists? The ecology of the Thicket needs preserving, and ecological balance is liable to be fragile. In a short time the "pearls" would lose the very values for which they were to be preserved.

The conservationists' criticisms do not stop at this point, however. They add at least three more complaints to their arsenal. The first concerns historical values; the second involves the place of water-flow in preserving ecological balance; the third involves the elusive but all-important "wilderness experience." One of the reasons for trying to prevent the death of wilderness areas is to secure for coming generations the experience of untrammeled, abundant wilderness: an experience fundamental to the pioneer spirit and which does so much to make American history unique. How, one wonders, in the mill-race of technological and social change, is there going to be any sense of historical continuity if some features of the historical past are not retained? We lecture to young people about what the United States has been, and expend jawbone energy exalting our forebearers. But we are careless enough about perserving any ties that would visually, physically, and without oratory, *show* the reality and the value of historical roots. I am often reminded of William Faulkner's admonition that wherever one may go or whatever one may become, however radical, one should, before making his future and himself, take at least "one backward glance at Monticello." It is not that the past can literally *make* the future for us; but it can afford our very unhistorical generation some sense of perspective and of familiarity—and of balance. Conservatives who oppose conservation might do well to think on this point, when they come to consider the Big Thicket.

But this is to add still a fifth argument to the conservationist's file—the argument from historical continuity. Those who might wish to deemphasize this argument will still continue to point out that a "wilderness experience" cannot be secured in the String of Pearls or any longer anywhere in East Texas, unless a sizeable chunk of the Big Thicket can be definitely and finally put out of reach of the bulldozers. Finally, conservationists protest, the ecology of the Big Thicket, like that of the Florida Everglades, cannot be preserved unless its water table can be preserved also—unchanged and unpolluted. The presence of subdivisions and new roads, and of increased water pollution, would in time wreck the Pearls one by one, by cutting off their water supply or polluting it, or both. Doubtless the Pearls could then be sold back to the lumber companies to be bulldozed for pine plantations: and everyone could live happily ever after.

Such arguments as these, unfortunately, have had no influence on the timber industry, which moved immediately to embrace—and advertise—the String of Pearls, both in its glossy pamphlet, *Stewards of the Land* (distributed free to the unwary), and in a powerful, well-financed public relations campaign. A large portion of that campaign has involved sending hired public relations men throughout Texas to talk garden and service clubs into passing resolutions favoring the 35,000 acre National Monument on the pretext that this was to back Senator Yarborough—instead of to undercut his stand for a larger park.

The first reaction of conservationists to the new stance of the lumber industries was one of jubilation. For decades lumber interests had insisted that none of the Thicket was worth saving. Now they had at last come around to admitting that at least patches of it were worthy of preservation. But the jubilation was short-lived. Word soon came that the Beech Creek Unit and the Cypress Creek Unit had been cut, and their stands of virgin beech and magnolia lost forever. Equally discouraging was the realization that lumber company cutting schedules had rapidly accelerated. In particular, it seemed strange that magnolias should be singled out for cutting. Professor McLeod has pointed out that magnolias are one of the basic emblems of the Big Thicket—and now, suddenly, the slow-growing trees were being cut down by the hundreds. How could that be? At the going market rate, a 100 year magnolia is worth very little—less than five dollars in railroad ties, to be precise. On a tour of the Big Thicket, Supreme Court Justice William O. Douglas pointed out magnolias that had been cut by timber companies on publicly owned highway rights-of-way. Was there no way to stop this needless plunder, he asked? None, was the reply. No politician would dare to enforce right-of-way laws in counties where the lumber companies control the economic and political machinery.

Lumber executives, questioned by Dennis Farney, a *Wall Street Journal* reporter who had become interested in the Big Thicket, replied that increased cutting schedules were simply a response to increased market demands for lumber. They added that the proposed park units had been cut by small landowners over whom the big companies had no control. It was not long after the appearance of Farney's article that still a third area, in the center of the Profile Unit, was taken over for a red flag subdivision. Simultaneously, cutting was going on in the lower reaches of the Profile Unit near Saratoga, as towering cypress were felled into Pine Island Bayou and their stumps and branches left to rot. It seemed very generous to conservationists that the lumber companies should make such a pious display of generosity in willingly allowing the String of Pearls to be included in an inadequate Big Thicket National Monument—particularly since they were willing to let the Pearls be cut down one by one in the meantime.

A reaction, however, finally set in—and not a moment too soon. The cries of conservationists, the political acumen of the Big Thicket Association, and the potential for endless bad publicity finally brought the lumber interests to declare a moratorium on cutting in the units set aside for the national monument. The moratorium was officially begun in July, 1967. It is probably true that, so far as concerns the areas inside the boundaries of the "Pearls," the moratorium has not been violated. It is also fair to point out that one lumberman, Arthur Temple of Diboll, complied with the moratorium through the very expensive procedure of closing down a lumber mill dependent on the hardwood timber in and around the Neches Bottom Unit. Mr. Temple is widely known as the most farsighted and open-minded of East Texas' lumbermen, and his compliance involved both personal expense and a great deal of trouble. His actions and his attitudes require careful consideration when one comes to pass a verdict in the confrontation between the lumber industry and the Big Thicket.

From the conservationists' viewpoint, the lumbermen's moratorium proved a Pyrrhic victory. Newly applied cutting methods in the Big Thicket began to involve more than the simple cutting of hardwoods; rather, the bulldozers began to make their appearance as hundreds, thousands of acres were scraped bare after timbering. The end result was to be, not the old mixed pine-hardwood forest with its incredibly varied understory of shrubs, small trees and vines and its highly complex labyrinth of "ecological niches" supporting a wealth of bird, insect, and animal life: not this, but the endless geometrical lines of the pine plantation, a "biological desert" where the transient bird and animal population "had better carry knapsacks." Local people, both for and against the national park, studiously concede that attempts by the lumber companies (Temple Industries excepted) to render vast tracts of land unfit for inclusion in any park, large, small, or indifferent, are an open secret. They might well be wrong. But to the conservationist, the results are just the same.

In creating a national park, a great deal depends on the backing of the congressman within whose district the proposed park lies. Unfortunately the Big Thicket area was represented by Congressman John Dowdy, an arch-conservative. Dowdy was widely known as the lumber companies' man, and repeated efforts by conservationists failed to budge him from his adamant unconcern. A local lumber executive had, back around 1964, earned considerable fame for himself by snapping, "The Big Thicket? The way we're going, in ten years there won't be any Big Thicket!" Dowdy's personal sentiments were only slightly less acid. As quoted by Edwin Shrake in a recent issue of *Harper's*, Dowdy claimed that the Big Thicket was merely a "stinking mosquito-infested swamp": "I don't see how anything can be done about a park, no matter what the Sahara Club wants." A congressman who does not know, or want to know, the difference between the Sierra Club and the Sahara Club does not make an ideal proponent of conservationist measures.

Shrake's lament for East Texas is deeply felt by many, and certainly not just the conservationists. East Texas is trapped, he asserts, between a pioneer legacy and an industrial establishment which will destroy it:

> Not far from what is now Hoop 'N Holler Estates, weekend cottages for people fleeing Houston and Beaumont, the Indians used to bathe in hot mineral springs and drink crude oil as medicine. The springs are dried up now, panthers are seldom seen, bears wander in confusion as far north as

Lufkin, where they are shot trying to escape, and the oil of the Indians has been drilled in dozens of pools that bred boomtowns and formed such giants as Texaco. Senator Ralph Yarborough, a Texas Democrat, is trying to save a piece of the Big Thicket as a national park, but it is perhaps a vain hope. As much as they may feel blood kin to the woods and streams that have nourished them for generations, most of the people who live in the Big Thicket, and in the rest of East Texas, depend for their livelihood on the industries that are destroying them, and so they vote for candidates chosen by big companies.

The burden of Shrake's argument is embodied in a brief exchange between himself and a filling station attendant. Complaining about the noxious fumes from a nearby pulp mill, Shrake lamented: "If I lived in this town I'd burn that factory down." "If you lived in this town you'd work in that factory," was the reply.

To everyone's surprise, however, Congressman Dowdy finally introduced a bill, in 1968, to create a Big Thicket National Monument of from 35,000 to 48,000 acres. The bill was felt to be a shrewd but surprisingly generous move by lumber interests to head off a still larger park. (By then Senator Yarborough had upped his own park proposal to 100,000 acres and national conservationist organizations were talking in still larger figures.) Whether Dowdy might or might not have persisted in his bill is difficult to ascertain. He is, as this is being written (1971), awaiting trial for bribery.

The result of years of waiting, of proposal and counterproposal, thrust and counterthrust, turned out to be, from the cutting moratorium of 1967 well into 1970, more waiting and more uncertainty. A stalemate had been reached. Forced to bide his time, Senator Yarborough sought funds to make the Padre Island National Seashore and Guadalupe Mountains National Park into realities, while conservationists struggled to bring the information media and local and national conservationist groups around to their way of thinking. As they labored, the felling of trees continued, the face of the Thicket changed. Politics is a slow business; power sawing and bulldozing are not.

5

a study in patience

During the decades when lumber companies bulldozed and cut and the image of the park ebbed farther and farther away, more than one of those who had worked long and hard to protect the wilderness gave up in despair, or soured, or joined the opposition. It was understandable. Every time the goal seemed to come within reach a rumor would be spread, or a misunderstanding would arise within the association, and amidst the resulting confusion the dazzling image of a green, forever inviolate park would slide away again. Like, for example, the time a plan was suddenly revealed to drain the entire Lower Big Thicket for rice farms and cattle: courtesy of the Southeast Texas Resource Conservation and Development Project: courtesy of the U.S. Department of Agriculture. The idea was to bulldoze Pine Island Bayou, in the heart of the Traditional Thicket, turning it into a ditch with nice straight lines and no messy trees, animals, vines, or swamps in the way. Why not, conservationists asked, just go ahead and pave it? Why not pave the whole southeast corner of the state?

In the face of this and a hundred other pretexts, Lance Rosier never seemed to falter. When others felt sorry for themselves, he would walk silently into the woods to commune with a big cypress tree or fern-covered oak. Then he would come back and lead someone else—a biologist, painter, or reporter—back into the Thicket.

Lance's front door was open to anyone. The only person ever turned away from his shaded, vine-trellised front porch was a man who wanted to kill a lot of unusual tree frogs because he could get one hundred dollars for them. Lance remarked quietly that it was too late in the day to go out in the woods, and besides, it looked like rain. That was as close as Lance would come to an argument. It was also as close as he would come to being dictated to by the weather. His persistent labors as a guide and a spokesman finally

87

earned him the title "Mr. Big Thicket." Looking at him, you would not have suspected he was Mr. Big anything. Especially, you would not have suspected his persistence. He was frail and wizened. He would not have topped 125 pounds soaking wet; his eyes were gentle, and distant, and etched with smile-lines. Just looking at him, there was a lot you would never have known.

In fact, there were things about Lance even those who knew him best did not know. Not that he kept secrets; he just never got around to talking about himself. People could tell you that he never got beyond the sixth grade, and that he had begun learning the Latin names of plants and animals when he served as a guide for scientists back in the thirties, when they did a Big Thicket biological survey. And you could guess from the number of books and articles tucked away in nooks and crannies in his house that he had learned some more since then. People could also tell you that he never married, and that when other boys were busy playing football or getting jobs drilling oil wells or felling timber, Lance was out wandering the woods, learning where wild orchids grew and where there were egret rookeries. You did not need to be a genius to guess how much kidding—and how much cruel sarcasm—he had to take because of it. "In those days," he would drawl, "a man with a rosebush in his yard was called henpecked."

People in the Big Thicket, who had known Lance long before he became a favorite target for newspaper photographers, were entirely puzzled by his fame, and by the respect he earned: "Why," they would ponder, "he don't do nothin' but prowl these woods lookin' for varmints. Why, that's all he's ever done. And those people come clear from Washington just to see him." No matter how you looked at it, it just did not make sense.

Looking at his shy, weather-beaten face, you could not keep from wondering, sometimes, whether he had ever been young. Or, more prosaically, whether he had ever hunted squirrel or shot birds, or cut down a tree. When he was lying near death at a hospital in Beaumont a wizened old country woman came up to a group of Lance's friends and said how much she had loved Lance: "He was the best dancer. We used to dance all night long at parties when we were young." Lance's friends were astonished. No one had ever seen him dance. No one had ever imagined the possibility.

Some admiring writers portrayed Lance as a sort of latter-day Saint Francis of Assisi. Though I never saw him deliver a sermon, like Saint Francis, to a bird or a snake, I have seen him pick up a big golden spider in his hand, talk to it, and set it back down on its web without getting bitten—a triumph I did not duplicate. He had an incredibly green thumb; if he could not grow a bush or flower in his yard, you could be pretty sure it would not grow anywhere else in the Thicket. He loved all living things, in an intense, personal way that was at the same time sober and dispassionate. But that did not qualify him for canonization.

Then, too, there was his sense of humor. A one-ring circus was making the rounds in East Texas when one of its meager collection of animals, a baboon, passed away. The circus went on to its next thrill-packed engagement at a sawmill clearing and the animal was dumped in a ditch. No one in the Thicket knew what it was. Finally everyone decided to go ask Lance Rosier. Lance leaned over the back of the pickup and cocked his head.

"Well," he mused, "from the look on its face, and its stooped neck, and the callusses on the seat of its britches, I'd say it's a retired East Texas domino player."

Lance was not a trained scientist; nor did he know every single tree, creek, or swamp in the sprawling 400,000 acre region. He knew the Lower Thicket—particularly the "Traditional Thicket" where he was born and raised; the Upper Thicket he knew less well. Yet he could give you the Latin and the common name of almost any of the area's thousand varieties of flowering plants.

The thousands of people who went on Lance's tours over the years remember them as unique hybrid crosses between botanical lecture and jeremiad. The net result was pleasant, but it left one with much to think about. Supreme Court Justice William O. Douglas, in his *Farewell to Texas*, captures one of Lance's bouyant moods:

> The dogwood and the redbud made even cutover land seem gay and joyous. But the rhododendrons and azaleas we saw were the most striking of all. The order of flowering for the shrubs of the Big Thicket is as follows: cross vine, yellow jasmine, hawthorn (of which there are 20 species), azalea and rhododendron, wisteria, dogwood and smoke tree. All but the smoke tree were on display when we hiked Menard Creek. And the showiest were the azaleas that sometimes stood so thick that they looked like a planted hedge. The flower that caught my eye was a huge pink one as large as the orchid one buys at the florist for his lady.
>
> Lance produced a low blueberry in bloom that fruits in the early summer and is much prized for the kitchen. He also showed me a tree type of blueberry that fruits in the fall and furnishes much feed for the birds. He found a small shrub more poisonous than poison ivy or poison oak.
>
> "But it is useful to man," he added. The sap is used to make varnish. It is also useful to animals. Fifteen species of birds and the cotton-tail rabbit feed on it. . . .
>
> A few huge cypress—more than two feet in diameter and probably 200 years old—had somehow escaped the lumber operations that had ravaged Menard Creek and stood in splendor in damp places. We stopped to make a boring in a loblolly pine; it had a diameter of 14 inches and was thirty-two years old.
>
> "It's now big enough to be commercial," Lance volunteered.
>
> A white-eyed vireo was singing. A belted woodpecker streaked across the treetops. Somewhere in the distance a pileated woodpecker was hammering in a hardwood.

It would be like Lance to know which plants were useful in making varnish, or treating diabetes, or making fine lacquers or folk medicines. He was never so happy as when he could show the usefulness of wilderness to some doubting Thomas.

A typical Rosier tour would take you through the hardwood and palmetto country along Pine Island Bayou. He would talk about resurrection ferns, epiphytes, and symbiosis, until the hulking skeletons of dead trees aroused your curiosity:

"Lance, what killed those big cypresses?"

"Oil wells, up on Batson prairie."

"You mean they struck a gusher up there, and the oil got in the bayou?"

Lance would lean down to look at a wildflower.

"No, it was salt water. They let it overflow in here. It killed all the cypress clear downstream twenty miles."

"Didn't they try to stop it?"

Before he replied you knew the answer.

"They don't care. I've seen them, when we get a heavy rain, they go out and take the gates out of the overflow ponds. They figure no one will notice it when the bayou's full."

"But they have to build ponds now. I mean, big enough to hold the salt water."

"What's the use of ponds, if you let it all back into the bayou?"

He would then straighten up and talk about the world's tallest cypress that had been found down in the river bottom not long ago, or about the cypress over on Village Creek that biologists had speculated was probably the world's oldest—older even than the old ones in the Everglades. Not till later would he let drop that there was an even bigger cypress back in the swamps: dead, killed more than ten years ago by oil well overflow. The next time you saw an oil well you would have something to think about besides millionaires in Stetson hats with society ladies.

Lance was to have many opportunities for a jeremiad. There was, for example, the heron rookery. For years he had taken people to a swamp near the Trinity River to see the rookery, where over three hundred water birds nested. In 1963 he took a friend along the old logging trail to the rookery only to find the birds were dead: they had been sprayed from the air with insecticide. White herons, blue herons, water turkey were strewn haphazardly around the rookery. Nests were tangled with rotted flesh and bone; a putrid smell hung in the air.

"Was it a mistake?" people asked.

"No," he would answer, "How could it have been? You couldn't miss the rookery from the air. And it's not right next to any field."

"But who would do a thing like that?"

"Oh, somebody fighting the park. They want to make it so that there's nothing left for the park. So they sprayed it from an airplane."

"But who could do that? Who could want to?"

He would then look off into the woods and change the subject. The newspapers, for a while, carried stories about the poisoned rookery. Then the matter dropped from sight. Football season would be starting soon. You have to keep your perspective.

One of the best known writers to learn from Lance was Berton Rouché, who described an outing involving Lance and conservationist Ernest Borgman in the *New Yorker*. The day began with a trip up the famous "ghost road," a half-abandoned logging spur between Saratoga and the town of Bragg. Once a busy stop on the Santa Fe Railroad, Bragg is now abandoned; nothing exists there but an old hotel and encroaching forest. The "Ghost" is a phosphorescent light which has been seen off and on at night for years by local passers-by. Legend has it that it is the lantern of a hunter who went to sleep on the ghost road when it was still a spur railroad track and had his head cut off by a train. The ghost is looking for its lost head by lantern light.

After many twists and turns Lance led the two men to the highpoint of the trek: a huge, three-pronged magnolia at the intersection of Polk, Hardin, and Tyler counties, which had been known for generations, locally, as the Witness Tree. A thousand years old, it was the world's largest magnolia. The path to the tree led into the Tight-Eye country, off dim tire tracks:

> It was real Thicket—a forest floor of fallen trees swamped with brush and briar, and understory of holly and dogwood and gum and oak and maple and hawthorn trailing vines and Spanish moss, and a soaring, pillared canopy of beech and magnolia and loblolly pine. There was no sky, no sun, no sense of direction. We climbed over logs and circled sloughs and ducked under hanging branches, and every log and every slough and every branch looked very much like the last. There were no landmarks. There were only the double welts of the old blazes. We picked our way from blaze to blaze—missing a blaze and circling back and finding it and moving on to the next. We walked for a mile and a half.

A clearing then appeared, and Lance pointed to a big grey stump covered with woodpecker holes. This, he explained, was the famous and historic Witness Tree:

> "That stump?" I said. It was a very big stump. It was fifty feet high and at least four feet in diameter. But still it was just a stump. "That stump is the Witness Tree?"
>
> Borgman was staring at it too. "What happened, Lance?" he said.
>
> "They poisoned it three years ago," Rosier said. "They pumped it full of lead arsenate. I can show you the holes they bored in to put in the poison. I came in with the experts that made the investigation. We found the holes stopped up with little wooden pegs."
>
> "But why?" I said. "Why would anybody do a thing like that?"

94

"It sounds crazy," Borgman said.

"Yes sir," Rosier said. "But there isn't any mystery about it. They did it for a warning. They were some of the folks that didn't want the National Monument."

The killing of the Witness Tree had made the papers too, just as it was to make the pages of the *New Yorker* some months later. When confronted, the management of one lumber company replied that it had never heard of the tree.

"That," Lance often mused, "was flat-out impossible. They know all the big trees around there. All the lumber companies have catalogues of big trees."

So far as I know, he never laid the blame on any one company or person. If asked, he changed the subject.

There were occasions, however, when he would go out of his way to point out a villain. Two years ago Lance asked me if I would drive him out along an unfamiliar rutted clay road. Miles later he finally asked if I would stop and look at something interesting that he had been saving for me. We pulled over to the side under the shadow of pine trees. Ahead of us a hawk circled through the calm afternoon. Beside us stood a billboard.

"But Lance, I thought this was supposed to be part of the Big Thicket National Park."

He nodded sadly.

"It was. Right in the middle of it."

"You mean the Department of Interior decided it wasn't good enough for the park?"

"Oh, it's plenty good enough. It's a beautiful woods. But they're cutting it up for vacation homes, weekend places," he grimaced. "The U.S. Government won't do anything about it."

The billboard (ten feet high, twenty feet long) proclaimed that this was Hoop 'N Holler Estates, and listed financial arrangements through which the urban tourist could participate in "life in a real wilderness." I had hoped that the announcement of plans for a Big Thicket National Park would put an end to the needless bulldozing. So much for hope.

"Drive on in," Lance grinned, "Take some snapshots. Take all you want."

A quarter mile from the entrance sign was an air-conditioned frame shack, decked out in fluttering orange plastic streamers. A sign on its roof stated, once more, the attractions of life in a "real wilderness." Behind the shack roads had been cut, subdivision-style, through what biologists had specified as a uniquely rich botanical area. Massive brush-heaps two to three times the height of the car rotted beside the road. Gum trees, magnolias, yaupon were piled up like matchsticks.

"The man who did this is from Livingston," Lance offered. "He says he's helping

95

the Big Thicket by bringing in jobs and people in here. A month ago a man from the Audubon society came out here and begged them not to wreck this part of the woods. The man who owns this got on a bulldozer and knocked down some more trees, just to show us. He said it was his land, bought and paid for. He even let us take a picture of him next to the bulldozer.

"And there's another thing," he pointed, "those signs all around here say No Hunting. And they hunt in here all the time."

Sure enough, a man carrying a shotgun walked across the road ahead of us. He disappeared into the brush on the other side of the road, passing under a No Hunting sign. Behind him the foundations of a new house rose incongruously.

"If the law was halfway straight they'd all be in jail," Lance snapped. "There was nine units that was going to be in the park. This one—you can see what they did to it. Cuts the middle right out of the Profile Unit. Cuts it right in two. And that's the heart of the park.

"They timbered the Beech Creek Unit. Soon as we set it aside for the park. And they want to cut the Loblolly Unit. You know, that's the last big stand of virgin pine in Texas. Four hundred years old. Here: you want to take a picture?"

He climbed onto a toppled tree trunk and stared glumly around. The Thicket was getting its publicity now. People were getting to know about it. But it was getting destroyed even faster than it was getting known.

We spent an hour taking pictures, then headed back to Saratoga. On a table on Lance's front porch lay a copy of the *Pineywoods Press* (Promoting Recreational and Industrial Growth in East Texas), which Lance was glad to loan out. Headlines in the six sheet tabloid enthusiastically proclaimed the opening of Hoop 'N Holler Estates. I said goodby to Lance and headed back to the urban sprawl of Houston.

That was not the first vacation subdivision to be cut into the Big Thicket. Conservationists made publicity for the region, and the real estate promoters, seeing a chance to make a fast buck, capitalized on the publicity by bulldozing what the conservationists were trying to save. Lance watched them go one by one, the orchid bogs and the stands of insectivorous plants, the heron rookeries and the thick magnolia-studded woods, the wild places he had known as a boy where you could hear nothing but frogs, birds, and the thunder of wind in big trees. Now they were estates with plastic flags and barbecue stands; and the emblem of the Thicket was not the ivory-billed woodpecker but the subdivider's bulldozer.

You never heard of Lance getting sick. He was wiry, but not weak, and he could hike with the best hikers. No one knew his age. He had been claiming for over a decade to be sixty-two, and no one could prove any different.

"Why, he was afraid no one would go out into the Thicket with him if they knew how old he was," his friends would explain. "He was afraid those women's clubs wouldn't

come here to Saratoga and hike with him, if they thought he was going to fall down in the woods from the heat. He's been sixty-two as long as I can remember."

Every year in Saratoga there is a Big Thicket Get-Together. It is a time for country fiddlers, a beauty pageant, gossip swapping between conservationists. Lance always enjoyed it; it was a chance to see all of his friends. During the 1969 Get-Together he stepped out onto the main steps of the old high school building in Saratoga; suddenly something gave way, and Lance found himself on the ground, his left hip broken. He was rushed to a hospital in Beaumont.

For a while it appeared that he was mending well. It was not as long as people thought it would be before he was back in his house at Saratoga, and then out on the street again—walking with a cane. He would throw that cane away one of these days, or know the reason why, he said. And he would get back out into the Thicket. People believed him, even though he seemed weaker and his limp increasingly pronounced. Winter came, and he remained home, alone in the house. Leaves made a brown carpet on the lawn; bare tree limbs scratched against house sidings. Lance quit talking about throwing away his crutch.

Toward the end of February, I dropped in on him, bringing two friends, Roy and Karen Hamric. Lance was sitting quietly on his grey, paint-flaking porch. Frail and tired, he insisted nonetheless on showing us the Big Thicket; he needed to walk a lot he explained, since his hip broke. We got into the car and headed out. It was a grey winter day with the wind beginning to warm from the south and the sun breaking through. Lance asked us to stop the car on a sand side road, under a grove of big magnolias. On one side of the road was a huge live oak.

"My grandfather came here before the Civil War," Lance said. "He had six slaves. In those days people thought he was a rich man because of the slaves. The day he came he planted that big oak tree," he pointed to the massive trunk and mossed, soaring branches. "His house stood yonder."

"Where that hunting shack is?"

"Yes. It was a big old house. But it burned down."

Lance limped ahead, pointing out plant species, confirming recent bear sightings, explaining how the lumber companies sprayed seven thousand acres along the Ghost Road to kill off everything but pulp pine. He leaned over and struck a beer can with his cane.

"Look. Civilization has been here."

Half a mile off the road he stopped at a dead tree whose core had been blasted open leaving a hole big enough to drop a shoebox in. Ivory-billed woodpeckers had done it, he explained. Maybe there were a dozen left in the world; if you drained the Thicket, the way the rice farmers and ranchers wanted, they would be gone.

The trouble was, people out here did just as they pleased. There weren't any game laws; poaching was the rule, the wardens never arrested local people. The open places were closed off by hunting leases now, and you couldn't get in to them any more. They killed so many deer on one hunting lease, running them with dogs, that they had to bring in new deer from the King Ranch in South Texas. And they killed those fast as they could bring them in. There would be plenty of game for everyone, if they would just enforce the law. But the poachers had a free hand. They had killed out most of the frogs and alligators. They were electrocuting the fish in the water holes with telephone generators: stunning them, picking them up off the top of the water.

"Maybe the Gospel of Ecology is slow in getting here," Roy shook his head.

"They won't let it across the county line," Lance answered.

To the question whether his leg would heal Lance replied that he had finally got used to the idea that he'd always have to walk with a cane. When he was young he'd been hit by a car, and when he mended one leg was longer than the other. But he refused to walk with a limp. Every day for hours he labored up and down steep stairs in his aunt's house until he was exhausted. It took almost a year, but he managed finally to walk straight. He would start getting back into the deep woods again this spring, limp or not. He told us to ask people to keep coming to see the Thicket with him.

The winter sun was already beginning to sink. Lance posed for a picture in front of his grandfather's live oak tree. He slumped faintly with weariness; his eyes were gentle and, in the fading light, distant. That is how his friends would want to remember him, peering off into the Thicket, seeing what the land had been before bulldozers, asphalt, power saws; thinking of him, they would ask how he had managed not to sour on people, whether he really believed there would be anything left in the end but wrecked woods and cheap weekend subdivisions. He had fought them year by year, step by step, always losing, heeded too late. Yet he was like some quiet piney lake toward sunrise, serene and at peace.

A month later, March 12, 1970, Lance Rosier was dead, of cancer. He was survived by three brothers and two sisters, and a covey of newspaper articles stating that Mr. Big Thicket was dead.

When the last eulogy was read, and the funeral done, and people had just about gotten used to the idea of Lance not being around any more, one of his brothers went over to Lance's house and cut down the shrubs and dug up the flowers and climbing vines planted over the years with such care, so that the house was now barren and isolated on packed dirt. The windows were covered over with sheets of corrugated tin, and the tree limbs were barren. What had been a recess among thick green shadows now looked like a sharecropper's shack on some worn-out patch of delta land. No birds would sing there, even now that spring was coming back by fits and starts to the Thicket country. There would be no burst of azalea now near the sagging porch.

6
the big thicket
gets its hearing

Had Lance lived that spring he would have seen the first real step toward creating a Big Thicket National Park: a United States Senate Hearing, in Beaumont, May 12, 1970. Until it has a hearing, no bill to create a park or monument can be moved out of committee onto the Senate floor. And if its hearing is inconclusive, its hopes of reaching a vote are small.

Senator Yarborough's testimony, which began the hearings, started with personal reminiscences of his youth in East Texas and moved quickly to consideration of our national crises in land, water, and people. Americans, he said, richly blessed with natural resources, have too long acted without regard for the future. But they have suddenly awakened to some harsh realities:

> As the nation becomes more crowded and the vast majority of citizens live and work within the urban areas, the demand for a quiet, natural place for relaxation, recreation, and spiritual restoration becomes far more acute. There are over three and one half million people who live within 100 miles of the Big Thicket, and over 13 million within 250 miles, an easy day's drive. These millions of people, and millions of more throughout the nation, need natural recreation areas and are seeking places where they can enjoy the relaxing influence of a quiet forest, or a tree shaded place by running waters, filled with the wonders of nature.

Turning from the national and international environmental crisis, the senator went on to consider the economic impact and value of the proposed park, a value which lumber company arguments emphatically neglect:

In a recent study sponsored by the National Park Service, conducted by Dr. Ernest S. Swanson, "Travel and the National Parks: An Economic Study" (1969), these conclusions were reached: "The computations made show that national parks contribute as much as $6.4 billion to the sales of a multitude of firms throughout the nation. From this amount, personal income of $4,762,530,000 is generated. . . . Travel to the National Park System resulted in $952 million in taxes for the Federal Government in 1967.

"These results do not represent the further indirect effects upon regions in which National parks are located. Over a period, other spending results from expansion of local activities directed toward creating attractions in addition to natural beauties and wonders of the region."

As an example, specialized provisions for hunting, fishing, boating, swimming, picnicking, and sightseeing on Indian Reservations are often undertaken through the stimulus of the flow of visitors to National parks. The study relates that economists in Colorado estimate that over $1.2 billion is generated from hunting and fishing alone.

The study concludes its summary with this comment:

"The National Park System with appropriations of around $102 million contributes at least 45 times this amount to the American people in the way of increased income—or more than 55 times the appropriations when income is stated as gross national product."

The advantages of a national park in the Deep East Texas area, which has not received much economic benefit from the tremendous economic growth the state has experienced since World War II, must be considered:

Rather than injuring the economy of the area . . . it is clear that . . . a national park would give it a much needed boost, and would help in the development of a broader and stronger economic base rather than one founded primarily on lumbering.

The proposed park, moreover, would involve the investment of only 3.3 percent of the acreage of the affected counties.

The senator's testimony, solid and to-the-point, covered ground well known to most conservationists. The testimony of John W. Fultrell, president of the Sierra Club of Louisiana, came as a surprise to the densely packed courtroom. By 1980 the once rural State of Louisiana, Fultrell explained, is expected to have a population of over four million, largely concentrated in a ten mile wide strip along the coast. What access will these people have to a hardwood forest? The hardwoods of Louisiana are disappearing at the incredible rate of 111,000 acres a year. If their destruction continues at this rate, by 1990 there will no longer be hardwood forests in Louisiana. There is little hope of saving even small tracts of this forest in Louisiana, where conservation is absolutely at the

bottom of the state's list of priorities. If the people of Louisiana are to have access to a natural hardwood forest, it must be through the protection of Texas' Big Thicket.

Not all the arguing was to be done by conservationists. Ollie R. Crawford, representing the Texas Forestry Association, explained that three years ago the National Park Service proposed a 35,000 acre national monument. The Texas Forestry Association endorsed the recommendation, and backed a voluntary moratorium on timber cutting in the proposed monument units, which lumber executives literally "walked the land" to point out to Park Service representatives. Far from intentionally cutting the Big Thicket, he said, the lumber companies ". . . have regrown the Big Thicket that was practically destroyed in the past." The Texas Forestry Association, Crawford contended, has never fought the park.

Senator Yarborough leaned over the rostrum and stared pointedly at Crawford.

"Isn't it true that the Texas Forestry Association has had two men traveling full-time around Texas getting endorsements for the 35,000 acre National Monument?"

Crawford's denial of the senator's charge was followed by a second question.

"Isn't it true that, just before this hearing, the Texas Forestry Association brought in reporters from all over the state on a chartered plane to give them propaganda against the park?"

Crawford replied that it was just the normal way of "telling one's own story." He did not look up as he said it.

It was not until later in the day that a new rumor suddenly surfaced: Village Creek was to be stripped of timber and dammed to provide "recreational facilities." That part of the Big Thicket would have to lie under twenty feet of water, safe from conservationists and students of ecology. Texas (which already has more lakes than Minnesota) was in dire need of a new lake.

The general contention that the Big Thicket has immense scientific value was reinforced by Dr. Daniel E. Willard, of The University of Texas Department of Zoology. In ecology as in other scientific disciplines, Dr. Willard insisted, new discoveries come about through the comparison of both one's primary experiment and one's "control" experiment. Our industrial intrusions into nature constitute a sort of primary experiment in ecology. But we need to keep primitive areas which are essentially unchanged by our intrusions and which constitute our "control" experiment. The Big Thicket is one such area. Dr. Willard added that in science new things come from unexpected places. The Big Thicket is a storehouse of unexplored genetic information. There is no telling how much it may do for us, if its remarkable diversity can receive permanent protection.

Testimony continued from early morning through midafternoon, when the senators embarked on a helicopter tour of the region. The hearing, Senator Bible said, was the best he had seen on a proposed national park. Unfortunately, the helicopter that afternoon lost its way en route to the Indian reservation at the northwest corner of the

110

Thicket and strayed over farm and industrial areas. "I began to wonder," said Dempsie Henley, "if the Texas Forestry Association hadn't arranged for the helicopters." Apparently, however, Senator Bible, the leaders of the National Park Service, and a multitude of reporters saw enough to be convinced. The general opinion that evening was that the Big Thicket had seen its finest hour.

The next day Senator Yarborough was supposed to be in Central Texas to help dedicate Lyndon Johnson's birthplace. But he had picked up a rumor to the effect that Ralph Yarborough wasn't going up to Saratoga because the Big Thicket hearings were just a show, and there wasn't going to be any national park. To refute the rumor the senator arrived unexpectedly at the annual Big Thicket trail-ride and get-together at Saratoga, full of enthusiasm. "They say the Thicket hearings don't mean anything," said Yarborough to a crowd of two hundred Thicket supporters. "That's just hogwash. It might not be tomorrow, and it might not be a year, but there is going to be a Big Thicket National Park. There will be more rumors that if there is a park they will close your schools and there will be no jobs. That's hogwash, too. The schools will stay open. And you'll hear rumors that the government will come in and throw people off their land if there's a national park. That's hogwash. And the people starting those rumors know it's hogwash. National parks create jobs. Pulp timber gives you a crop every ten years; tourists give you a crop twelve months of the year."

In one respect, events very nearly proved the senator correct; but in another respect they have left the issue in doubt and confusion—a confusion which still awaits resolution. During his final days in the Senate, Ralph Yarborough was able to pass his Big Thicket National Park Bill. At the last minute, however, an amendment was added to limit park size to "100,000 acres or less," in spite of the senator's efforts to secure a larger acreage. It proved impossible to bring a similar bill, sponsored by Congressman Bob Eckhardt, before the House in time for passage, however. The Big Thicket National Park had thus been headed off once more. The entire legislative process had to begin again, in the next session of Congress.

This time, however, the park had to face a veritable smokescreen of potential park legislation. Texas politicians rushed, upon the defeat of Yarborough's bill, to introduce Big Thicket National Park bills of their own. Rather than coming to an agreement about the proposed park and throwing the full weight of the Texas congressional delegation behind one measure, Texas' national representatives chose to perpetuate a tangled thicket of proposals. Once their proposals were made, moreover, they sat back and did nothing (exceptions to this rule include Congressmen Jake Pickle and Bob Eckhardt); as interest in the Big Thicket receded.

In general, three different park sizes were proposed. Newly elected Senator Lloyd Bentsen proposed a park of "not more than 100,000 acres," while Senator John Tower introduced a bill calling for an 81,472 acre park with an additional 18,528 acres in recreational areas along lakes in Texas' National Forests (total: 100,000 acres). In the House, Congressman Earle Cabell introduced a bill authorizing the 35,000 acre monument proposed by the lumbermen, while Congressman Pickle, and others, introduced bills providing for a park not more than 100,000 acres. Only Congressman Eckhardt introduced a bill protecting a really sizeable portion of the Big Thicket, 191,000 acres. For both its ingenuity and its importance to conservation, Eckhardt's bill merits consideration here.

Bob Eckhardt has spent a good deal of time hiking in, and pondering over, the Thicket. His park plan, which shows real ecological insight, closely follows the rivers, bayous, and creeks of the region. Exceptions include the minute but biologically precious Clear Fork Bog, the virgin loblolly pines northwest of Batson, the Hickory Creek Savannah and 40,000 acres of rich timberland in the Saratoga-Sour Lake-Kountze Triangle—deep woods which Archer Fullingim calls the "Holy Ghost Thicket." The remaining 150,000 acres consist of interconnected corridors along the Neches River, Pine Island Bayou, and Menard, Big Sandy, Cypress, Turkey, and Village creeks.

Maps of Eckhardt's proposed Big Thicket National Park made two things clear. The first is that his projected park boundaries would conserve segments of every sort of ecosystem in the Thicket region, with the exception of prairie. The second is that the bill will scarcely hurt the lumber companies, who stand to lose mainly swampy bottomland where not even loblolly pine will grow. (Pine trees, needless to say, are the basic source of timber that lumber companies are presently interested in.) When lumber company representatives cry in anguish that a large Big Thicket National Park will put the Texas Forest Products Industries on the ropes, those droplets staining their two-hundred-dollar-suits are one hundred percent crocodile tears.

One could argue that the proposed park corridors are too narrow to protect the Thicket, that such thin strips of vegetation are insufficient to withstand the immediate influx of cafes, service stations, and quasi-Disneylands that will be constructed as close to the park as possible. A Small Thicket National Park, however, would be even less able to withstand tourist pressure than the park Eckhardt proposes. And until lumber companies want to sell out their holdings in the region, there will be a great deal of land along the park boundaries that will definitely not be for sale.

And so the matter stands. Lacking the political fulcrum it so desperately needs, a suitable park bill awaits action. Lacking even the most minimal environmental protection, the Big Thicket recedes daily before the bulldozer, the brush hog, the power saw. For conservationists the hour is late, decisive action is necessary. For many politicians, there is always plenty of time. Unless the public says otherwise.

7

the shape of a park

In the past, we have looked upon our national parks primarily as scenic areas, secondarily as camping and hiking facilities. There is nothing wrong with either of these functions. But, taken in themselves, they are incomplete. What is lacking is some realization of the educational function which a national park can fulfill. We have long appreciated the beauty of wilderness areas, but we have awakened only recently to what they can teach us.

The cause of this awakening is not far to seek. The human race has entered the seventh decade of the twentieth century with the sudden realization that it has so raped and polluted its environment that the future existence of life itself has been undermined. The rivers, the air, the soil, the farthest oceans are polluted; depleted forests, minerals, water supplies dwindle before our eyes; the spaces we thought were wide open are now crisscrossed with roads and power lines, the cities and towns merge together into gigantic, sprawling "megalopoli"—smoke-canopied, decaying, socially unstable. And the world's unendingly expanding populations signal the spectre of rising world famine.

How did it happen? How did perpetual progress veer to such a sudden halt? Our visions of a better, freer, technologically perfected world have come apart in our hands.

The biologist, the ecologist, the environmentalist have a simple, clear-cut answer to our questions, an answer we can ignore, they argue, only at our peril. For centuries, they insist, we have been mauling our environment without any understanding, either of the environment or of our dependence on it. We have acted as if we could hack away at one part of the world without affecting all the others—as if we could cut down the trees without silting up the streams, and pollute the skies without affecting our lungs; as if we could douse our farms with chlorinated hydrocarbon insecticides and not kill off the birds that eat the insects that quickly develop a resistance to our insecticides. We have acted without knowledge. And now it is necessary to instill in all people a knowledge and appreciation of our environment as quickly and decisively as possible: before it is too late.

Few national areas are more suited for instilling an awareness of the variety of interrelationships necessary to sustain the balance of nature than the Big Thicket. But it will require bold visionary insight to make full use of the Thicket's educational potential. What follows are suggestions intended to ensure that a visit to the proposed park will be both an aesthetic and an educational experience—educational in a sense far removed from classrooms, lectures, and pedantry.

One of the early plans for preserving the Big Thicket included a scenic road winding down the full length of the Profile Unit. Such a road, conservationists protested, would have been in some places nearly as wide as the unit itself, and would have necessitated cutting many of the trees and bushes which it was the park's function to preserve. Why bring car noises, litter, and exhaust fumes into the heart of the wilderness? There are enough of them already, outside.

Yet the basic idea of giving people a chance to see untrammelled wilderness is a good one, and ought not to be easily given up. What must be given up is not the possibility of a view of the Thicket for those unwilling or unable to hike but the supposed necessity of making the trip by car. The possibility of a monorail or cable car system should be considered, which would take prospective visitors to widely varying plant and animal communities—without disturbing those communities even as much as would be done by bands of hikers. Monorail passengers would be able to visit a cypress swamp, a heron rookery, an alligator pond, a beaver dam, an orchid bog, a fern valley, a pine forest, a sandy, beech-shaded creek, a bayou, a grove of big trees. They would be able to observe the birds, insects, vines, and animals of the treetops as well as those along the ground; the inside of deep thickets would be open to them as well as the forest roof. And neither rain nor wind nor cold nor blistering heat would deter them from their appointed rounds.

Probably the first objection to such a project is its projected cost. But a monorail system charging a minimal fee could pay for itself over the years—partly by attracting tourists to such a unique way of seeing wild nature. Even were the expense never to be repaid in dollars, however, it would be repaid in an increased appreciation of nature by countless hundreds of thousands of Americans.

Monorails by no means exhaust the possibilities for painlessly imparting an understanding and appreciation of environment. There are aspects of nature which cannot be seen while in motion, or even when one is hiking slowly down a trail. The animals and plants of ponds and waterways, for example, are not easily observed by the hiker; nor are the birds of swamps and deep thickets; nor are the systems of the subsoil—rootwebs, crayfish and rodent burrows, and insect nests. Some means is needed to make these as apparent and as significant to the park visitor as the roadside trees and flowers. Suppose, for example, that the visitor could observe not only the surface of a cypress swamp but the fish and animal life in its waters? Or, suppose it were possible to observe a heron rookery from within its boundaries instead of from a lookout point many yards away? No miracle of engineering genius would be required to make this possible: only the use of one-way glass and the willingness to build observation areas both above and below ground level. Hawks, eagles, beaver colonies, perhaps even the ivory-billed woodpecker, would in this way be observed without being disturbed. The park visitor would experience the feeling of encountering deep wilderness without deep wilderness having been eradicated by park visitors.

In the lobby of the Visitors' Headquarters in the Great Smoky Mountains National Park one will find both a scale model of the local mountains and exhibits depicting the kinds of plants and animals to be found within the park. In the Big Thicket, such maps and exhibits ought to be developed to an extent unheard of in a national park. A central headquarters should be constructed containing not only a huge relief map of the Big Thicket region but a museum detailing the full variety of the area's animal and plant life as well as laboratory facilities for visiting scientists—of whom there will be many. The relief map should do far more than simply depict relative elevations and obvious topographic features like rivers, creeks, and swamps; it should depict in a graphic way the different ecosystems within the thicket, along with the soil types and indigenous animals and plants unique to these ecosystems.

Grouped around this central area should be at least nine large museum areas, one for each of the eight distinctive ecological areas of the region and a ninth devoted to the principles of ecology generally. In presenting the eight different Thicket ecosystems every effort should be made to ensure, first, that where possible live specimens should be used in place of dead and, second, that the entire spectrum of life should be covered. It is always possible to construct exhibits of plastic leaves, papier-mâché toadstools, and plaster stumps. But the park visitor would rather see live ferns, grasses, and trees, and real birds, turtles, armadillos, and fish. The problems involved in using live exhibits wherever possible would be more than made up for by their intrinsic interest: even if it involved creating sandy hillslopes, running creeks, acid bogs, and cypress swamps, and then planting them with native trees and vines. There is no reason why a museum exhibit has to be built in a small room behind glass, sheltered from rain, wind, and sun. Nor is there any reason why it must always consist of synthetic trees and stuffed birds. A Big Thicket museum ought to be as alive in every way as the Thicket itself.

It should also be as diverse and many-sided as the Big Thicket. The museum area dedicated, for example, to the mixed pine-hardwood forest should contain exhibits of the sorts of birds, insects, ferns, reptiles, amphibians, and mammals ordinarily found there together with an explanation of how they are dependent on that particular habitat for

their survival. The hiker who then strikes out into a mixed pine-hardwood area will know how to identify and appreciate the animals and plants that he will encounter as well as, hopefully, to understand the manner in which each is dependent on the others for its existence.

The same would hold for the ninth area, dedicated to an explanation of environmental systems generally. How many of us know that a fully developed beech forest requires years to appear, and can exist only after a whole series of other vegetation-types has appeared and passed away, finally creating the moist, deeply shaded surroundings in which beech groves flourish? How many of us are aware of the way in which DDT and other chlorinated hydrocarbons (or, for that matter, radioactive materials) are gradually concentrated in "food chains" until their effect becomes lethal to the animals at the top of each chain? Birds like the bald eagle and the peregrine falcon, for example, have been found to contain so much insecticide in their fatty tissues that they often can no longer reproduce. How many of us know that the same DDT is present in the tissues of all Americans—above all in mother's milk? A museum that can drive home some of the simplest principles of ecology to thousands of visitors annually may cost the taxpayer some money to construct and maintain. But in a million years, and if it were made of solid gold, it could never cost as much as ignorance of ecological principles will cost in the next twenty years.

The same general approach should apply to each of the regional museums scattered throughout the park. Starting from the central museum, where he could get a general view of what the Big Thicket is like, the visitor could then proceed to submuseums in whatever region he would like to explore; these latter would explain in much greater detail what is in the area, as well as suggest nearby hiking paths, observation areas, and canoe trips. Park visitors could thereby get both a general and a very local orientation—the park would be made accessible to them in every possible sense.

The various park "submuseums" could be tied together by the monorail system, which could make brief stops at each, picking up and letting off visitors. It would cut down automobile pollution and automobile traffic throughout the area, and the monorail system could make specially prepared stops along its path so that sightseers could, for example, walk across a bridge suspended over a tupelo swamp or orchid bog, or inspect a "champion" tree.

Would a monorail system destroy the wilderness character of the Big Thicket, bringing just one more element of urban gadgetry into the heart of the deep woods? What will become of the isolated character of the Big Thicket if an elevated railroad is built all over it? Such questions are understandable, but they fail to take account of the protective features of the monorail. A national park is visited annually by hundreds of thousands of sightseers who can hardly be kept within the confines of camping areas to satisfy those who would keep parks pure wilderness preserves. Better monorails than the trampling of hundreds of thousands of tourists. There are ways, moreover, to adapt monorails to wilderness conditions. The monorail supports and tracks could be painted the colors of the wilderness; the monorail pathway could be fitted into its surroundings so as to be scarcely visible; the Thicket will do the rest, camouflaging pipes and I-beams with vines, lichens, and Spanish moss. Monorails, moreover, are quiet. And, finally, there is no need to build a monorail through the heart of wilderness areas. One hundred feet from the edge of roads, clearings, prairies, the Thicket is thick; the wilderness exists at its borders as in its depths, and there is no need to penetrate its depths to make the monorail ride authentic—and unforgettable.

Important as ecology is, there is more to the Big Thicket than its ecology. There are its legends and its history, which also deserve to be preserved and presented to the visitor. I can remember standing on the porch of an original pioneer cabin at Cade's Cove, in the Great Smoky Mountains National Park, one April day some years ago, gazing out across a deserted valley from the cabin clearing. It seemed to me that I could gain, from that experience, some sense of the loneliness, the grandeur, and the hard work that molded pioneer character. I have had the same experience in the Big Thicket, in deserted cabin clearings where there was no sound but silence and birdcries, and the wind far off in the pines. For the moment time was rolled back, and it was possible to see woods, fields, and wild birds as the settlers must have seen them. There is no good reason, of course, why we should live in the past—even assuming that we could do so. But the sense of the past and of origins provides a very useful sense of perspective, and an understanding of national regional character. Precisely when change is necessary and inevitable, that understanding is most helpful.

The past cannot be conserved in the way that an ecosystem can. But every attempt should be made to preserve log cabins, in their original settings, along with log barns and corncribs, and old farm utensils: wheelbarrows, crosscut saws, scythes, hoes, plows, harnesses. It should be continued in the Big Thicket National Park and made as complete as possible.

The same holds for the railroads, the oil wells, and the lumber mills of the region. At the town of Moscow, in Polk County, there are old steam locomotives which were once used to haul timber and which are now rusting into oblivion on old siding tracks. There is an effort now to do something to preserve these technological relics. Perhaps part of the answer is to make them into national park exhibits, or even to put them back to work hauling passengers in reconstructed, reupholstered railroad cars, along old logging tracks. The first oil well ever drilled in the Southwest was sunk at Saratoga in 1864. It is still there, unmarked and overlooked, by the roadside. Alongside it are oil well derricks and discarded tools which would by themselves constitute interesting exhibits, if they could be brought together in one place and explained. The chaotic, exciting story of the early oil industry deserves to be told. Since Texas' oil industry began on the borders of

the Big Thicket, the Big Thicket is the logical place to tell its story.

The same sort of efforts should be made to preserve the surviving relics of the original lumber industry. The lumber industry ought to jump at the chance to tell their side of the Big Thicket Story. They have felt all along that conservationists have given a slanted and unrealistic account of the wonderful job which the lumber companies have done to preserve the ecological values of the Big Thicket and to provide a sumptuous living for the average lumber worker. Perhaps, then, the lumber companies would be delighted to create a Big Thicket Museum of Lumbering to explain their past and present practices to the public.

There has been a long-standing argument between those who believe that national parks are for the sake of pure wilderness and those who believe that "Parks are for People," to quote the well-known slogan. In any national park or wilderness area it is a touchy, very difficult matter to see to it that somehow both of these viewpoints are met and responded to. In the Big Thicket the problem will inevitably emerge again as conservationists finally concur on the shape of the proposed park. If the suggestions put forward here were to be followed, however, the people could be brought to the park without the park being damaged by the people. The Big Thicket National Park should provide for untold thousands of visitors a striking experience: a whole education that is never boring.

8

conclusion

The Big Thicket is a remarkably many-sided and intriguing place, which contains many surprises. If this book has managed to make this many-sidedness and fascination evident, then it has to a great extent succeeded in its task. Whatever the degree of success or failure, however, there remain a few more facts to be added, in order to keep the record, and the basic perspective, straight. These facts include the corporate tangle in which the Big Thicket finds itself ensnared, and the economics of park acreage. But they also include one final reference to the beauty of the region—a beauty which, if it tends to get lost in economic and biological statistics, is rarely lost on those who experience it.

Most Texans assume that their state is owned, and controlled, at home. In the case of the Big Thicket, at least, this is not so. Today only one of the companies that scalped the original wilderness, and then allowed it to regrow, is still in control of a sizeable portion of Big Thicket land. This company, Temple Industries, is not involved in the rush to eliminate hardwood trees. But other corporate owners—the ones referred to briefly in the preface—are involved in the rush.

No one writes braver ecology editorials than *Life* magazine—unless, perchance, it is *Time* magazine or *Sports Illustrated*, also owned by Time, Inc. One waits in vain, however, for these giants of the American magazine industry to descant upon the fate of the Big Thicket. Several years ago when *Sports Illustrated* writers descended on the Thicket to do an article, conservationists were delighted by the prospect of national publicity. The article, however, did not appear. It died mysteriously in *Sports Illustrated's* editorial rooms primarily because, I am told, it came out flatfooted for a Big Thicket National Park. This last spring a *Life* editor and several assistants came to the Thicket to do an article on the elusive ivory-billed woodpecker. (Long thought to be extinct, the ivory-bill was photographed on May 28, 1971, in Southern Louisiana—but not by a *Life* photographer.) Needless to say, the article in question has never appeared, in spite of promises of quick publication.

There does appear to be some connection between *Time's* editorial conscience and its corporate self-interest. For Time, Inc. (through its subsidiary, Eastex) owns 600,000 acres in East Texas, over 100,000 acres of which fall within the four-country area being considered as a locale for a Big Thicket National Park. Of *Time's* 600,000 acres, 150,000 have already been converted into pine plantations. Another 330,000 acres await the same fate. This will make a total of 480,000 acres (750 square miles) transformed into straight lines of slash pine, interspersed with bare clay and decorated with a handful of grass species. Where hardwoods (oaks, magnolias, beech trees, hickories) try to regrow, they will be cut down or extinguished with herbicides. The bulldozing timetable as given by Ollie Crawford, Eastex's public relations man, runs as follows: In 1971 *Time's* subsidiary Eastex will bulldoze 4,000 acres in East Texas; in 1972 the figure will rise to 6,000 acres, and in 1973, 8,000. To be sure, one-fifth of Time, Inc.'s Texas lands will be left in hardwoods (though it is possible that these too, eventually, will be bulldozed and re-planted). But four-fifths of their land (80 percent) will be transformed.

Time, Inc. is followed closely by Santa Fe Industries (Chicago), International Paper (New York), Owen-Illinois (Toledo), and U.S. Plywood-Champion Papers (New York). Southland Paper Mills, Inc. (Lufkin, Texas) is the one locally based concern which has done its share of bulldozing in the region. Thirty-eight percent of Southland is owned by St. Regis Corporation (New York). The same bulldozer and slash pine mentality that motivates Time, Inc. also dictates the decisions of Santa Fe, which owns 600,000 acres in East Texas through its subsidiary Kirby Lumber, as well as International Paper (500,000 acres) and the other concerns listed above, with the exception of Temple Industries. The demolition, where it exists, is complete and thorough. There will be no regrown Thicket this time.

Lumber and pulpwood lobbyists reply to the protests of environmentalists, and newly concerned local people that pine plantations are really marvelous places. Lumber company brochures show lavish displays of wildflowers among the pine stalks. Lumber company representatives have recently begun speaking of the wonderful hunting that goes on between the geometric rows. In fact, they have gone out of their way to inform East Texas hunters of the wonders that await them in their newly "rejuvenated" and "re-forested" slash pine gardens. But such claims are patently false. Dr. Clarence Cottam of the Welder Wildlife Foundation puts it fairly and simply:

> There aren't many game or wildlife species that dwell in the forest of near
> pure culture of slash pine. In fact, many of the pines are not very good as

wildlife foods. Some of them in moderate amounts serve as food supplements. Generally, I think we can say that a monoculture of a single species is never a good wildlife habitat.

Population in an extensive area of predominantly slash pine would in all probability be quite low. Some insects are associated with it. Therefore we can expect some of the vireos, flycatchers, and warblers to subsist, assuming that there are other species in sizeable abundance in the mixture of slash pine. Rodents, of course, feed to some extent, on the seeds and some birds would get nourishment from the seeds. Squirrels would do fairly well if there are other species to go with this. But if it is predominantly a single culture of slash pine, nothing would do well.

Dr. Cottam's remarks are low-key. But one has a feeling they are going to be heard, particularly by those who have so far ignored the cries and accusations of conservationists.

Incidentally, in a "monoculture of a single species," predators which normally keep tree-infesting insects under control are largely absent. The result is a plague of, for example, pine borer beetles, which must then be controlled through large doses of insecticides sprayed from airplanes. One waits eagerly for some lobbyist to inform East Texans that insecticides are really great at improving fishing in the local streams, and aiding the health of the local populace.

In his speech before the Senate Hearing of June, 1970, Senator Ralph Yarborough underlined the economic arguments for establishing a Big Thicket National Park. At that time many conservationists, however much in sympathy with the Senator, felt that his figures must somehow have been exaggerated. It turns out, however, that they may have been on the conservative side. If one assumes around two million visitors per year to the proposed park, spending an average of $71.00 each, one comes up with $142,000,000.00 per year tourist income spent in Texas thanks to the park. (The figure for *per capita* spending by tourists is furnished by the Texas Highway Department.) If one assumes that the park will cover 200,000 acres, and that all of this is good timber-growing land, then the total income from timbering this land will come to $13,000,000.00 per year. This last sum is obtained by multiplying the average yearly financial yield per acre of Texas forest lands ($43.50) times the total acreage. When the two sums are compared, one comes up with a *ten-to-one* ratio in favor of the park! Even if the ratio were five-to-one, or even three-to-one, the beneficial economic impact of the park would be immense. Figures like these do not add up to an economic depression.

But perhaps, a critic might ironically suggest, the depression would be borne by the companies which would lose land to the park. Who could blame a corporation for fighting to keep its head above water? There are two replies. In the first place, most companies which stand to lose land in the Thicket own countless millions of forested acres throughout the United States. (For example, International Paper controls 6,980,000 acres, with cutting rights on another 16,000,000 acres in Canada. Owens-Illinois controls 1,300,000 acres. Champion controls 1,968,000 acres.) Land losses by these firms in Southeast Texas would scarcely be serious. Moreover no one company would foot the whole bill, or even a sizeable part of it. And, finally, they would be *paid* for their land. It is not a matter of piracy.

Still, is it as simple as that? Do the "vested interests" really have that little to lose? The answer is, that at least one of their public representatives *says* they have that little to lose. In a Texas Daily Newspaper Association seminar in September, 1971, Ollie Crawford, public relations man for Eastex and Time, Inc., conceded to the assembled reporters that even Congressman Eckhardt's 191,000 acre park would not significantly hurt the companies. To make himself clear he repeated this conclusion a second time. The writer, who was invited to the seminar to present the conservationist viewpoint, found himself staring back in amazement at a half dozen reporters who were puzzling through the same question he was: *But if it won't hurt them, why are they fighting it so hard?* Unfortunately, Crawford left before anyone could find the answer. Surely there must be such an answer. To date, however, no one, including myself, has been able to find out what it is. If Time, Inc., with its "mere" 600,000 acres of timbered land in the United States cannot be hurt by the creation of a Big Thicket National Park, how can the other giant corporations?

Conservationists, however, feel that they have little time to ponder the question. Not only is the corporation bulldozer present in increasing numbers; the first real effects of the urban avalanche are now being felt in the Thicket. It has not been very long since the towns on the southern perimeter of the Big Thicket were remote, sleepy villages where farmers traded stories over the backs of pickup trucks and wagons and the spring rains left dirt roads knee-deep in standing water, and life went on pretty much untouched by the quickening pace of Beaumont and Houston. Twenty years ago to drive from Houston north to Conroe or northeast to Cleveland was to enter a world of deep pine forests, lonely bottomlands, tenant cabins, and cornfields: a world as different and as separate from the new skyscrapers on Main Street as if it had been shut off somewhere in the Mississippi Delta and forgotten.

Now the metropolis is reaching out, and where there were deep forests there are, overnight, weekend subdivisions and full-year subdivisions, plate-glass supermarkets, bulldozed creekbeds, and new paved roads. Once-isolated towns are becoming part of the metropolitan areas of Houston and Beaumont, and the real estate developers are beginning to look beyond even the first ring of outlying towns to the forests and pastures. If there is nothing to halt the flood of city-sprawl and city-flight, in thirty years what will be left of Southeast Texas' piney woods—for lumbering or anything else? The extent of urbanization and its effects will reach far beyond what anyone has imagined. One would think that the lumber industries would jump at the idea of a Big Thicket Environmental

Area, safe forever from the urban explosion, capable of producing necessary timber and wilderness experience for countless generations. One would think that the people of the Gulf Coast Megalopolis would stand up and demand that the Big Thicket region be saved, a morning's drive away from the noise, frustration, and polluted air that are to be increasingly their lot.

If they have not until recently done so, it is because the realization of the extent of environmental change has been slow to dawn. Each of us goes his own way, immersed in the problems and surroundings which directly affect us. Only rarely do we step back and look at the whole picture, in the long view. It is no surprise, therefore, that the human race only recently has stepped back to see what are the long-term prospects for its environment. Those prospects have been serious enough to force a reassessment of man's entire effect on nature. In the process, assessments of the value of places like the Big Thicket have significantly changed. Now, suddenly, we want to save them. We never miss the water 'till the well runs dry—or is about to.

The arguments stressed above to justify saving the Thicket have been biological, historical, and finally, economic. There is something paradoxical in the idea that one should be required to justify saving a part of our environment. In all rational conscience, shouldn't it be the other way around? Those who wish to pollute, strip, simplify, or otherwise diminish nature should instead be required to produce justifying arguments for their actions—good arguments, not just flimsy rationalizations for short-term profits. But since that is, unfortunately, not the way things are, two more arguments will be considered here before bringing this brief survey of the character and value of the Big Thicket to a close.

One of these arguments has already been touched on, namely, the Thicket's status as a last surviving region in which the traditional deep Southern forest can be preserved. There are those who deny that such forests need, or deserve, to be saved in a wilderness state. Such persons, I believe, limit themselves to the Walt Disney conception of a park as a place for canyons, geysers, mountains, and weathered rocks. To be sure, there is nothing wrong with any of these. Only, it is time that we began to reverence life, in its myriad manifestations, more than huge landscapes of unliving rock. Isn't it living things which, in the end, should merit our fascination, and respect—and protection?

For those who agree with the import of this last question, the case for the Thicket is all but established. Where else on our continent will one find such an outpouring of life as here, as the western limits of Faulkner's wild Southern woodlands, his "impenetrable jungle of waterstanding cane and cypress, gum and holly and oak and ash?" When Faulkner wrote, the virgin Southern forest had already been cut, and only the ghosts of its massive, sprawling wilderness remained, to haunt the second and third growth saplings, and the memories of old men. Today, from Virginia through Mississippi to Texas, the entire Southern Evergreen Forest is being weeded out root and branch, for slash pine plantations. The wisdom of this giant transformation is severely open to question. But there is no question that at least some portions of the original forest type should be preserved. There is, to repeat the argument of J. W. Fultrell, no national park dedicated to the Southern hardwood.

It may not quite seem to fit here, among discussions of forest types and ecological transformations, but there is an old story about President Calvin Coolidge that bears repeating. Coolidge was sightseeing in San Francisco when one of his aides, desperate to keep a conversation going, remarked, "I see they've just recently painted the cable cars in San Francisco." Coolidge thought a while and then nodded curtly: "On one side, at least." Coolidge's skepticism is instructive. There are some who remain skeptical under any bombardment of facts and arguments. They refuse to be convinced.

For those who remain unconvinced about the Big Thicket, I can offer only one further argument. In the spring, when the flowers burst from fields of new grass and big green leaves of the grapevines drag in creekwater and clamber up to the remotist treetops, slide a canoe into Village Creek, or Big Sandy, or the Neches River, and drift quietly under the overhang of willows, and cypress, and wateroak. Perhaps you will see a heron stalking along the white sand bars, or a hawk pivoting over the standing pines. Probably you will hear the wind move high up in the cottonwoods, making a rain-like patter. Then, in the stillness, ask yourself whether this was meant for all generations, henceforward, or only for this generation; for fifteen, possibly twenty years more.

appendix

representative trees and shrubs of the big thicket

1. upland communities

trees

Longleaf Pine	*Pinus palustris*
Shortleaf Pine	*Pinus echinata*
Sweetgum	*Liquidambar Styraciflua*
Blackjack Oak	*Quercus marilandica*
Bluejack Oak	*Quercus incana*
Post Oak	*Quercus stellata*
Black Hickory	*Carya texana*
Shagbark Hickory	*Carya ovata*
Winged Elm	*Ulmus alata*
Black Cherry	*Prunus serotina*
Sugarberry	*Celtis laevigate*

shrubs and small trees

American Plum	*Prunus americana*
Flatwoods Plum	*Prunus umbellata*
Carolina Holly	*Ilex ambigua*
Georgia Holly	*Ilex longipes*

Parsely Hawthorn	*Crataegus Marshallii*
Allegheny Chinkapin	*Castanea pumila*
Eastern Redbud	*Cercis canadensis*
Tree Sparkleberry	*Vaccinium arboreum*
Pawpaw	*Asimina triloba*
Rusty Blackhaw	*Viburnum rufidulum*

2. beech-magnolia communities

trees

Beech	*Fagus grandifolia*
Southern Magnolia	*Magnolia grandiflora*
Loblolly Pine	*Pinus taeda*
Swamp Chestnut Oak	*Quercus Michauxii*
White Oak	*Quercus alba*
Sugar Maple	*Acer saccharum*
Mockernut Hickory	*Carya tomentosa*
Shagbark Hickory	*Carya ovata*
White Ash	*Fraxinus americana*
Carolina Basswood	*Tilia caroliniana*
American Holly	*Ilex opaca*
Shumard Oak	*Quercus Shumardii*

(The beech-magnolia community is taken by Professor Claude McLeod to define the Upper Thicket; in the Lower Thicket beech is largely replaced by swamp chestnut oak to create a swamp chestnut oak-magnolia community. These two nearly identical communities constitute a "matrix vegetation" linking all other Big Thicket plant communities together.)

shrubs and small trees

Redbay	*Persea Borbonia*
Common Sweatleaf	*Symplocos tinctoria*
Witchhazel	*Hamamelis virginiana*
American Snowbell	*Styrax americana*
Yaupon	*Ilex vomitoria*
Two-wing Silverbell	*Halesia diptera*
American Wistaria	*wisteria frutescens*
Arrowwood Viburnum	*Viburnum dentatum*
Mapleleaf Viburnum	*Viburnum acerifolium*

Carolina Buckthorn	*Rhamnus caroliniana*
Inkberry	*Ilex glabra*
Swamp Cyrilla	*Cyrilla racemiflora*

(Most of these shrubs and small trees create an "understory" throughout the areas of Big Thicket matrix vegetation. Arrowwood viburnum and Carolina buckthorn are more frequent in the Upper Thicket, mapleleaf viburnum, inkberry, and swamp cyrilla in the Lower Thicket.)

3. savannah communities

trees

Longleaf Pine	*Pinus palustris*

shrubs and small trees

Southern waxmyrtle	*Myrica cerifera*

4. bog communities

trees

Sweetbay	*Magnolia virginiana*
Swamp Tupelo	*Nyssa sylvatica* var. *biflora*

shrubs and small trees

Piedmont Azalea	*Rhododendron canescens*
Inkberry	*Ilex glabra*
He-huckleberry	*Lyonia ligustrina*
Rabbiteye Blueberry	*Vaccinium virgatum*
Poison-Sumac	*Rhus Vernix*

5. palmetto-baldcypress-hardwood communities

trees

Baldcypress	*Taxodium distitchum*
Water Oak	*Quercus nigra*
Willow Oak	*Quercus Phellos*

shrubs and small trees

Dwarf Palmetto	*Sabal minor*

6. baygall communities

141

trees

Sweetbay	*Magnolia virginiana*
Redbay	*Persea Borbonia*
Water Oak	*Quercus nigra*
Blackgum	*Nyssa sylvatica*
Carolina Ash	*Fraxinus caroliniana*

shrubs and small trees

Common Buttonbush	*Cephalanthus occidentalis*
Possumhaw Viburnum	*Viburnum nudum*
Large Gallberry	*Ilex coriacea*

7. floodplain forest communities

trees

Baldcypress	*Taxodium distichum*
Water Tupelo	*Nyssa aquatica*

8. streambank communities

trees

River	*Betula nigra*
American Sycamore	*Platanus occidentalis*
Boxelder	*Acer Negundo*
Planertree	*Planera aquatica*
American Elm	*Ulmus Americana*
Cherrybark Oak	*Quercus falcata*
Overcup Oak	*Quercus lyrata*

shrubs and small trees

Black Willow	*Salix nigra*
Blueberry Hawthorn	*Crataegus brachyacantha*
American Elder	*Sambucus canadensis*
Hazel Alder	*Alnus serrulata*
Possumhaw	*Ilex decidua*
Brook Euonymus	*Euonymous americanus*
Fringe-tree	*Chionanthus virginica*
Honeylocust	*Gleditsia triacanthos*
He-huckleberry	*Lyonia ligustrina*
Virginia Sweetspire	*Itea virginica*

American snowbell   *Styrax americana*
Sebastian's Spurge   *Sebastiania fruticosa*

ferns of the big thicket

	Cutleaf Grape Fern	*Botrychium dissectum* (occasional)
	Virginia Grape Fern	*Botrychium virginianum* (rather frequent)
	Bulbous Adder's-Tongue	*Ophioglossum crotalophoroides* (rare)
	Limestone Adder's-Tongue	*Ophioglossum Engelmannii* (uncommon)
	Fragile Adder's-Tongue	*Ophioglossum nudicaule* (rare)
*	Adder's-Tongue	*Ophioglossum vulgatum* (uncommon)
	Cinnamon Fern	*Osmunda cinnamonea* (frequent where found)
	Royal Fern	*Osmunda regalis* var. *spectabilis* (frequent where found)
X	Japanese Climbing Fern	*Lygodium japonicum* (occasional)
X	Sword Fern	*Nephrolepis exaltata* (rare if escaped)
	Bracken	*Pteridium aquilinum* var. *pseudocaudatum* (only infrequent)
X	Spider Brake	*Pteris multifida* (rare)
	Alabama Lipfern	*Cheilanthes alabamensis* (infrequent)
	Wooly Lipfern	*Cheilanthes tomentosa* (rare)
	Purple Cliffbrake	*Pellaea atropurpurea* (rare if present)
	Wright's Cliffbrake	*Pellaea ternifolia* var. *Wrightiana* (very rare)
	Sensitive Chainfern	*Onoclea sensibilis* (frequent)
	Virginia Chainfern	*Woodwardia virginica* (rather frequent)
	Net Vein Chainfern	*Woodwardia virginica* (rather frequent)
	Chain Fern	*Lorinseria areolata*
	Ebony Spleenwort	*Asplenium platyneuron* (rather common)
	Little Ebony Spleenwort	*Asplenium resiliens* (rare if present)
	Southern Lady-Fern	*Athyrium Filix-femina* var. *asplenioides* (rather frequent)
	Blunt-Lobed Woodsia	*Woodsia obtusa* (occasional)
	Downy Shieldfern	*Thelpteris dentata* (occasional)
	Broad Beech Fern	*Thelypteris hexagonoptera* (rare)
	Southern Shieldfern	*Thelypteris Kunthii* (occasional)
X		*Thelypteris Torresiana* (rare)
	Marsh Sheildfern	*Thelypteris palustris* var. *Haleana* (rare)
X		*Thelypteris versicolor* (rare)
	Florida Shieldfern	*Dryopteris ludoviciana* (recently discovered)

Christmas Fern	*Polystichum acrostichoides* (infrequent)
Resurrection Fern	*Polypodium polypodioides* var. *Michauxianum* (common on trees)
Water Fern	*Azolla caroliniana* (common where found)

This list is compiled from Cory and Parks *Biological Survey of the East Texas Big Thicket Area*, 1938; from Donovan S. Correll, *Ferns and Fern Allies of Texas*, Renner, Texas: Texas Research Foundation, 1956; and from John K. Small, *Ferns of the Southeastern States*, Lancaster, Pa.: The Science Press, 1938. The help of Professor Correll and Geraldine Watson in compiling this list is deeply appreciated. An "X" to the left of a name indicates that the species in question is not indigenous to Texas, though it may be naturalized there. An asterisk indicates the *possibility* of the existence of a species in the Big Thicket.

fern allies of the big thicket

Whisk Fern	*Psilotum nudum*
Tall Scouring-Rush	*Equisetum hyemale* var. *affine* (occasional)
Southern Club-Moss	*Lycopodium adpressum* (occasional)
Foxtail Club-Moss	*Lycopodium alopecuroides* (occasional)
Carolina Club-Moss	*Lycopodium carolinianum* (very rare)
Meadow Spike-Moss	*Selaginella apoda* (occasional)
Riddell's Selaginella	*Selaginella Riddellii* (common where found)
Quillwort	*Isoetes melanopoda* (rare)

orchids of the big thicket

Yellow Lady's-Slipper	*Cypripedium Calceolus* var. *pubescens* (rare)
White Fringed Orchid	*Habenaria Blephariglottis* (uncommon)
Chapman's Orchid	*Habenaria Chapmanii* (rare)
Yellow Fringed Orchid	*Habenaria ciliaris* (occasional)
Small Wood Orchid	*Habenaria clavellata* (frequent)
Crested Fringed Orchid	*Habenaria cristata* (rare)
Southern Rein Orchid	*Habenaria flava* (rare)
Yellow Fringeless Orchid	*Habenaria integra* (rare)
Snowy Orchid	*Habenaria nivea* (occasional)
Long-horned Habenaria	*Habenaria quinqueseta* (probably extinct) (rare in U. S.)
Water Spider Orchid	*Habenaria repens* (frequent where found)

144

Snakemouth	*Pogonia ophioglossiodes* (frequent)	
* Spreading Pogonia	*Cleistes divaricata* (doubtful in Texas)	
* Three Birds	*Triphora trianthophora* (doubtful if in Thicket)	
Large Whorled Pogonia	*Isotria verticillata* (occasional)	
Little Ladies' Tresses	*Spiranthes Grayi* (occasional)	
Fragrant Ladies' Tresses	*Spiranthes cernua* var. *odorata* (infrequent)	
Slender Ladies' Tresses	*Spiranthes gracilis* (rather frequent)	
Florida Ladies' Tresses	*Spiranthes gracilis* var. *floridiana* (rare)	
Lace-Lip Spiral-Orchid	*Spiranthes X laciniata* (rare)	
Giant Spiral Orchid	*Spiranthes longilabris* (rare)	
Oval Ladies' Tresses	*Spiranthes ovalis* (rare)	
Gaint Ladies' Tresses	*Spiranthes praecox* (occasional)	
Spring Ladies' Tresses	*Spiranthes vernalis* (rather frequent)	
* Low Erythrodes	*Erythrodes querceticola* (very rare if in Texas)	
Southern Twayblade	*Listeria australis* (frequent where found)	
Bearded Grass-Pink	*Calopogon barbatus* (very rare)	
Grass-Pink Orchid	*Calopogon pulchellus* (rather frequent)	
Spring Coral Root	*Corallorhiza Wisteriana* (occasional)	
Crane-Fly Orchid	*Tipularia discolor* (rather frequent)	
Green Addersmouth	*Malaxis unifolia* (occasional)	
Crested Coral Root	*Hexalectris spicata* (very rare if present)	
Shadowwitch	*Ponthieva racemosa* (very rare)	

This list is compiled from Cory and Parks *Biological Survey of the East Texas Big Thicket Area* (1938); C. L. Lundell, *Flora of Texas*, Vol. III, Part III, *Orchidaceae* by Donovan S. Correll, Dallas; Southern Methodist University, 1944; and a list of Big Thicket wildflowers compiled by Geraldine Watson. Asterisks mark those species whose general distribution makes their existence in the Big Thicket area probable.

representative wildflowers of the big thicket

spring (march-april-may)

Beardtongue	*Penstemon Laxiflorus*	Roadsides, Sand Woods
Bluebonnet	*Lupinus texensis*	Roadsides, Pastures
Swamp Buttercup	*Ranunculus septentrionalis*	Bottomlands
Dogwood	*Cornus floridana*	Woods, Pine Uplands
Roughleaf Dogwood	*Cornus Drummondii*	Wetlands
Woodland Gerardia	*Gerardia aphylla*	Pastures, Sandy Woods
Green Dragon	*Arisaema Dracontium*	Damp Woods

Horse Gentian	*Triosteum angustifolium*	Damp Pastures
Indian Paint Brush	*Castilleja indivisa*	Roadsides
Southern Blue Flag Iris	*Iris virginica*	Marshes, Ditches
Yellow Iris	*Iris fulva*	Marshes, Ditches
Spider Lily	*Hymenocallis occidentalis*	Swamplands
Balespike Lobelia	*Lobelia spicata*	Roadsides
Varicolored Phlox	*Phlox Drummondii*	Sandy Land
Ranunculus	*Ranunculus Cymbalaria*	Damp Roadsides
Scarlet Pimpernel	*Anagallis arvensis*	Roadsides
Mock-orange	*Styrax americana*	Moist Woods
Azalea	*Rhododendron canescens*	Streambanks

summer (june-july-august-september)

Wing-rib Sumac	*Rhus copallina*	Woods, Fencelines
St. Andrew's Cross	*Ascyrum hypericoides*	Pine Savannahs
Snow-on-the-mountain	*Euphorbis marginata*	Roadsides
Monkey-Flower	*Mimulus alatus*	Streambottoms
Southern Swamp Lily	*Crinum americanum*	Brackish Swamps
Indian Plantain	*Cacalia lanceolata*	Acid Soils
Swamp Rose-Mallow	*Hibiscus Moscheutos*	Wetlands
Cut-Leaved Evening Gerardia	*Angalinis tenuifolia*	Pastures, Water Margins
Tall Yellow Primrose	*Oenothera laciniata*	Roadsides, Sandy Fields
Elephant's Foot	*Elaphantopus nadutus*	Woodlands
Carolina-Lily	*Lilium Michauxii*	Sandy Woods
Bunchflower	*Melanthium virginicus*	Damp, Acid Woods
Gentian	*Estoma exaltatum*	Roadsides, Damp Fields
Bluecurls	*Trichostema dichotomum*	Sandy Soils
Blue Mistflower	*Eupatorium coelestinum*	Woods, Bottomlands
Wooly Croton	*Croton capitatus*	Fencelines, Prairies

autumn (october-november)

Bottle Gentian	*Gentian Saponaria*	Bogs, Streambanks
Indian-Pipe	*Monotropa uniflora*	Moist Woodlands
Gay-Feather	*Liatris elegans*	Acid Soils
Southern Swamp Lily	*Crinum americanum*	Brackish Swamps
Black Nightshade	*Solanum americanum*	Streambanks, Thickets
Prairie Onion	*Allium stellatum*	Roadsides
Burmannia	*Burmannia biflora*	Acid Soils
Blackeyed Susan	*Rudbeckia*	Roadsides

| Lobelia | *Lobelia Reverchonii* | Bogs |
| Shadowwitch | *Ponthieva racemosa* | Streambanks |

winter (december-january-february)

Western Mayhaw	*Crataegus opaca*	Wetlands
Bluets	*Hedyotis australis*	Roadsides
Mayapple	*Podophyllum peltatum*	Woodlands
Sunnybells	*Schoenolirion croceum*	Acid Wetlands
Chaptalia	*Chaptialia tomentosa*	Sandy Soils
Witch-Hazel	*Hamamelis vernalis*	Streambanks
Spring-Cress	*Cardamine bulbosa*	Bottomlands

Entries in this index are taken from a list compiled by Geraldine Watson. Classifications are taken from Correll and Johnston, *Manual of the Vascular Plants of Texas*, Renner, Texas: Texas Research Foundation, 1970.

representative grasses of the big thicket

Redtop Bentgrass	*Agrostis alba*
Autumn Bentgrass	*Agrostis perennans*
Hairgrass	*Aira elegans*
Foxtail	*Alopecurus carolinianus*
Little Bluestem	*Schizachyrum scoparium*
Arrowfeather	*Aristida purpurascens*
Giant Cane	*Arundinaria gigantea*
Georgia Cane	*Aruxdo Donax*
Carpet Grass	*Axonopus affinis*
Rescue Grass	*Bromus unioloides*
Ripgut Grass	*Bromus rigidus*
Field Sandbur	*Cenchrus incertus*
Poverty Oatgrass	*Danthonia spicata*
Crab Grass	*Digitaria sanguinalis*
Goosegrass	*Eleusine indica*
Wild-Rye	*Elymus cannadensis*
Lacegrass	*Eragrostis capillaris*
Stinkgrass	*Eragrostis cilianensis*
Silver Plumegrass	*Erianthus alopecuriodes*
Sugarcane Plumegrass	*Erianthus giganteus*
Eastern Mannagrass	*Glyceria septentrionalis*

White Grass	*Leersia virginica*
Perennial Ryegrass	*Lolium perenne*
Witchgrass	*Panicum capillare*
Browntop Panic Grass	*Panicum fasciculatum*
Guinea Grass	*Panicum maximum*
Switchgrass	*Panicum virgatum*
Knotgrass	*Paspalum distichum*
Annual Bluegrass	*Poa annua*
Kentucky Bluegrass	*Poa pratensis*
Indian Grass	*Sorghastrum avenacium*
Blackseed Needlegrass	*Stipa avenacea*
Eastern Gamagrass	*Trypsacum dactyloides*
Southern Wildrice	*Zizaniopsis miliacea*
Yellow Nutgrass	*Cyperus esculentus*
Southern Nutgrass	*Cyperus rotundus*

This list was compiled from the *Biological Survey of the East Texas Big Thicket Area.*

representative vines of the big thicket

Climbing fern	*Lygodium japonicum*
Sarsparilla-vine	*Smilax pumila*
Bamboo-vine	*Smilax laurifolia*
Saw-brier	*Smilax glauca*
Cat-brier	*Smilax Bona-nox*
China-root	*Smilax hispida*
Green-brier	*Smilax Smallii*
Common Green-brier	*Smilax rotundifolia*
*Coral Green-brier	*Smilax Walteri*
Queen's Wreath	*Antigonon leptopus*
*Eardrop Vine	*Brunnichia ovata*
Clematis	*Clematis dioscoreifolia*
Virgin's-Bower	*Clematis virginiana*
Blue Jasmine	*Clematis crispa*
*Leather-Flower	*Clematis Viorna*
Red-Berried Moonseed	*Cocculus carolinus*
Cupseed	*Calycocarpum Lyonii*
Climbing rose	*Rosa setigera*
Wisteria	*Wisteria macrostachya*

*Dioclea	*Dioclea multiflora*
Poison ivy	*Rhus Toxicodendron*
Rattan-Vine	*Berchemia scandens*
Mustang Grape	*Vitis mustangensis*
Summer Grape	*Vitis aestivalis*
Muscadine	*Vitis rotundifolia*
Red Grape	*Vitis palmata*
Fox Grape	*Vitis vulpina*
Virginia Creeper	*Parthenocissus quinquefolia*
Pepper-Vine	*Ampelopsis arborea*
Cross-Vine	*Bignonia capreolata*
Trumpet Honeysuckle	*Lonicera sempervirens*
Black-eyed Susan	*Thunbergia alata*
Japanese Honeysuckle	*Lonicera japonica*
Trumpet Honeysuckle	*Campsis radicans*
Bottle Gourd	*Lagenaria siceraria*
Wild Balsam-Apple	*Momordica Charantia*
*Climbing Hemp-Weed	*Mikania scandens*

This list was compiled from D. S. Correll and M. C. Johnston, *Manual of the Vascular Plants of Texas,* Renner, Texas: Texas Research Foundation, 1970; and from H. B. Parks and V. L. Cory, *Biological Survey of the East Texas Big Thicket Area.* Plants rare in the Big Thicket are denoted by an asterisk.

representative birds of the big thicket

I. classification according to habitat

1. marsh and water birds

Water-Turkey	*Anhinga anhinga*
*Wood Ibis	*Mycteria americana*
Roseate Spoonbill	*Ajaia ajaja*
**White-Faced Ibis	*Plegadis chihi*
**White Ibis	*Eudocimus albus*
Double-Crested Cormorant	*Phalacrocorax auritus*
**Olivaceous Cormorant	*Phalacrocorax olivaceus*
Great Blue Heron	*Ardia herodias*
Green Heron	*Butorides virescens*

Little Blue Heron	*Florida caerulea*
Louisiana Heron	*Hydranassa tricolor*
Black-Crowned Night Heron	*Nycticorax nycticorax*
Yellow-Crowned Night Heron	*Nyctanassa violacea*
Cattle Egret	*Bulbulcis ibis*
American Egret	*Casmerodius Albus*
Snowy Egret	*Leucophoyx thula*
King Rail	*Rallus elegans*
Virginia Rail	*Rallus limicola*
Sora	*Porzana carolina*
*Purple Gallinule	*Porphyrula martinica*
Florida Gallinule	*Gallinula Chloropus*
American Coot	*Fulica americana*
*Least Bittern	*Ixobrychus exilis*
*American Bittern	*Botaurus lentiginosus*
X Sandhill Crane	*Grus canadensis*
Fish Crow	*Corvus ossifragus*
*Fulvous Tree Duck	*Dendrocygna bicolor*
Wood Duck	*Aix sponsa*
*Canada Goose	*Branta bernicla*
*Snow Goose	*Chen hyperborea*
*Mallard	*Anas platyrhynchos*
*Pintail	*Anas acuta*
Blue-Winged Teal	*Anas discors*
*Shoveler	*Spatula clypeata*
*Redhead	*Aythya americana*
*Canvasback	*Aythya valisineria*

2. thicket, baygall, dense undergrowth

*American Woodcock	*Philohela minor*
X Winter Wren	*Troglodytes troglodytes*
X Brown Thrasher	*Toxostoma rufum*
White-eyed Vireo	*Vireo griseus*
*Prothonotary Warbler	*Protonotaria citrea*
X Swainson's Warbler	*Lymnothlypis swainsonii*
X Bachman's Warbler	*Vermivora bachmanii*
*Ovenbird	*Seiurus aurocapillus*
*Northern Waterthrush	*Seiurus noveboracensis*
*Song Sparrow	*Melospiza melodia*

150

3. pine woods

**Brown-Headed Nuthatch	*Sitta pusilla*
*Black-Throated Green Warbler	*Dendroica virens*
*Pine Warbler	*Dendroica pinus*
*Pine Siskin	*Spinus pinus*
Bachman's Sparrow	*Aimophila aestivalis*
**Red-Cockaded Woodpecker	*Dendrocopos borealis*
*Chuck-Will's Widon	*Caprimulgus carolinensis*

4. savannahs, prairies, woods margins

*American Golden Plover	*Pluvialis dominica*
Roadrunner	*Geococcyx californianus*
*Eastern Kingbird	*Tyrannus tyrannus*
*Scissor-tailed Flycatcher	*Muscivora forficata*
Mockingbird	*Mimus polyglottos*
*Eastern Bluebird	*Sialia sialis*
Loggerhead Shrike	*Lanius ludovicianus*
*Chestnut-Sided Warbler	*Dendroica pensylvanica*
XPrairie Warbler	*Dendroica discolor*
Eastern Meadowlark	*Sturnella magna*
*Indigo Bunting	*Passerina cyanea*
*Dickcissel	*Spiza americana*
*Savannah Sparrow	*Paserculus sanwichensis*
*Grasshopper Sparrow	*Ammodramus savannarum*
Lark Sparrow	*Chodestes grammacus*
*Yellow-Shafted Flicker	*Colaptes auratus*
Red-Headed Woodpecker	*Melanerpes erythrocephalus*

5. hardwood and mixed pine-hardwood forests

Wild Turkey	*Meleagris gallopavo*
*Great Crested Flycatcher	*Myiarchus critinus*
Blue Jay	*Cyanocitta cristata*
Carolina Chickadee	*Parus carolinensis*
Tufted Titmouse	*Parus bicolor*
White-Breasted Nuthatch	*Sitta carlinensis*
*Yellow-Throated Vireo	*Vireo flavifrons*
*Solitary Vireo	*Vireo solitarius*
*Warbling Vireo	*Vireo gilvus*
*Parula Warbler	*Parula americana*

151

*Magnolia Warbler	*Dendroica magnolia*
*American Redstart	*Setophaga ruticilla*
*Scarlet Tanager	*Piranga olivacea*
*Whip-Poor-Will	*Caprimulgus vociferus*
Pileated Woodpecker	*Dryocopus pileatus*

II. classification according to type

1. predators

XWhite-Tailed Kite	*Elanus leucurus*
XSwallow-Tailed Kite	*Elanoides forficatus*
Eastern Red-Tailed Hawk	*Buteo jamaicencis borealis*
Florida Red-Shouldered Hawk	*Buteo lineatus alleni*
*Sharp-Shinned Hawk	*Accipiter striatus*
*Broad-Winged Hawk	*Buteo platypterus*
XMississippi Kite	*Ictinia misisippiensis*
*Cooper's Hawk	*Accipiter cooperii*
XHarlan's Hawk	*Buteo harlani*
XSwainson's Hawk	*Buteo swainsoni*
XGolden Eagle	*Aquila chrysaetos*
*Marsh Hawk	*Circus cyaneus*
XOsprey	*Pandion haliaetus*
*Pigeon Hawk	*Falco columbarius*
Florida Barred Owl	*Strix varia alleni*
Great Horned Owl	*Bubo virginianus*
Florida Screech Owl	*Otus asoi horidanus*
*Short-Eared Owl	*Asio flammeus*
Barn Owl	*Tyto alba*
XSaw-Whet Owl	*Aegolius acadicus*
XLong-Eared Owl	*Asio otus*

2. wood warblers

*Black and White Warbler	*Mniotilta varia*
*Prothonotary Warbler	*Protonotaria citrea*
XSwainson's Warbler	*Limnothlypis swainsoni*
XWorm-Eating Warbler	*Helmitheros vermivorus*
*Golden-winged Warbler	*Vermivora chrysoptera*
*Blue-Winged Warbler	*Vermivora pinus*
*Tennessee Warbler	*Vermivora peregrina*

152

*Orange-crowned Warbler	*Vermivora celata*
*Nashville Warbler	*Vermivora ruficapilla*
*Parula Warbler	*Parula americana*
*Yellow Warbler	*Dendroica petechia*
*Magnolia Warbler	*Dendroica magnolia*
XBlack-Throated Blue Warbler	*Dendroica caerulescens*
*Eastern Myrtle Warbler	*Dendroica coronata*
*Black-Throated Green Warbler	*Dendroica virens*
*Cerulean Warbler	*Dendroica cerulea*
*Blackburnian Warbler	*Dendroica fusca*
*Yellow-Throated Warbler	*Dendroica dominica*
*Chestnut-Sided Warbler	*Dendroica pensylanica*
*Bay-Breasted Warbler	*Dendroica castanea*
XBlackpoll Warbler	*Dendroica striata*
*Pine Warbler	*Dendroica pinus*
*Prairie Warbler	*Dendroica discolor*
XPalm Warbler	*Dendroica palmarum*
*Ovenbird	*Seiurus aurocapillus*
*Northern Waterthrush	*Seiurus noveboracensis*
*Louisiana Waterthrush	*Seiurus motacilla*
*Kentucky Warbler	*Oporornis formosus*
XConnecticut Warbler	*Oporonis agilis*
*Mourning Warbler	*Oporornis philadelphia*
*Yellowthroat	*Goethlypis trichas*
*Yellow-Breasted Chat	*Icteria virens*
*Hooded Warbler	*Wilsonia citrina*
*Wilson's Warbler	*Wilsonia pusilla*
*Canada Warbler	*Wilsonia canadensis*
*American Redstart	*Setophage ruticilla*
XBachman's Warbler	*Vermivora bachmanii*

3. sparrows

*Savannah Sparrow	*Passerculus sandwichensis*
*Grasshopper Sparrow	*Ammodramus savannarum*
*LeConte's Sparrow	*Passerherbulus caudacutus*
*Henslow's Sparrow	*Passerherbulus henslowii*
**Sharp-Tailed Sparrow	*Ammospiza caudacuta*
*Vesper Sparrow	*Pooecetes gramineus*
Lark Sparrow	*Chondestes grammacus*

Bachman's Sparrow	*Aimophila aestivalis*
*Chipping Sparrow	*Spizella passerina*
XClay-Colored Sparrow	*Spizella pallida*
*Field Sparrow	*Spizella pusilla*
*Harris Sparrow	*Zonotrichia querula*
*White-Crowned Sparrow	*Zonotrichia leucophrys*
*White-Throated Sparrow	*Zonotrichia albicollis*
*Fox Sparrow	*Passerella iliaca*
*Lincoln's Sparrow	*Melospiza lincolnii*
*Swamp Sparrow	*Melospiza georgiana*
*Song Sparrow	*Melospiza melodia*
House Sparrow	*Passer domesticus*

4. woodpeckers

*Yellow-Shafted Flicker	*Colaptes auratus*
*Red-Shafted Flicker	*Colaptes cafer*
*Ivory-Billed Woodpecker	*Campephilus principalis*
Pileated Woodpecker	*Dryocopus pileatus*
Red-Bellied Woodpecker	*Centurus carolinus*
Red-Headed Woodpecker	*Melanerpes erythrocephalus*
*Yellow-Bellied Sapsucker	*Sphyrapicus varius*
Hairy Woodpecker	*Dendrocopos villosus*
Downy Woodpecker	*Dendrocopos pubescens*
**Red-Cockaded Woodpecker	*Dendrocopos borealis*

5. rare or scarce birds

**Brown-Headed Nuthatch	*Sitta pusilla*
**Ivory-Billed Woodpecker	*Campephilus principalis*
**Red-Cockaded Woodpecker	*Dendrocopos borealis*
XSwainson's Warbler	*Lymothlypis swainsonii*
**Wood Duck	*Aix sponsa*
XWhite-Tailed Kite	*Elanus leucurus*
XSwallow-Tailed Kite	*Elanoides forficatus*
XMississippi Kite	*Ictinia misisippiensis*
XBachman's Warbler	*Vermivora bachmanii*
XLeConte's Sparrow	*Passerherbulus caudacutus*
XGolden Eagle	*Aquila chrysaetos*

Most of the categories in this list are incomplete. Possible exceptions are the

154

warblers and woodpeckers. Only those sparrows are listed which bear the word "sparrow" in their title; additions to the list of sparrows are therefore possible. The Peregrine Falcon (*Falco peregrinus*) and Bald Eagle (*Hailaeetus levcocephalus*) are possible additions to the list of rare or scarce birds. Both these latter and the Sparrow Hawk (*Falco sparverius*) might be added to the list of predators. The Mississippi and Swallow-Tailed Kites are listed only as "hypotheticals." The White-Tailed Kite was identified by the author in the Big Thicket in the spring of 1971.

The classification of a species under a given habitat does not imply that it can not be found elsewhere. Classification according to both habitat and type results inevitably in some duplications from list to list.

An asterisk (*) to the left of an entry signifies that it is migratory. Two asterisks (**) signify that it is rarely or infrequently seen in the Big Thicket. An "X" signifies that it is both migratory and rarely or infrequently seen.

This list has been compiled from several sources. Among these are: Mrs. C. H. Newsom and Mrs. Lynette McGaugh, "Spring Count 1967 May 4, Evadale, Village Mills, Hillister, Kountze and surrounding areas in Hardin, Jasper and Tyler Counties"; Mrs. Charles H. Newsom, compiler, "Spring Bird Count 1968 April 28, Hardin, Tyler, Jasper and Liberty Counties"; Mrs. Cleve Bachman, personal correspondence, September, 1970; Roger Tory Peterson, *A Field Guide to the Birds of Texas*, Boston: Houghton Mifflin Company, 1963; Olin Sewall Pettingill, Jr., *A Guide to Bird Finding West of the Mississippi*, New York: Oxford University Press, 1953.

representative reptiles of the big thicket

Alligator	*Alligator mississippiensis*
Chameleon	*Anolis carolinensis*
East Texas Sand Lizard	*Holbrookia propinqua propinqua*
Horned Toad	*Phrynosoma cornutum*
Pine Lizard	*Sceloporus undulatus undulatus*
Glass Snake	*Opisaurus ventralis*
Stripped Racehorse Lizard	*Cnemidophorus exlineatus*
Bluetailed Skink	*Eumeces fasciatus*
Ground Lizard	*Leiolopisma laterale*
Blind Snake	*Leptotyphlops dulcis*
Worm Snake	*Carphophis amena vermis*
Blue Racer	*Coluber constrictor flaviventris*
Black Snake	*Coluber constrictor constrictor*
Ringneck Snake	*Diadophis punctatus arnyi*
Indigo Snake	*Drymarchon corais couperi*
Chicken Snake	*Elaphe obsoleta confinis*

155

Spotted Chicken Snake	*Elaphe laeta*
Horn Snake	*Farancia abacura*
Puff Adder	*Heterodon contortrix*
Yellow-bellied King Snake	*Lampropeltis calligaster*
Speckled King Snake	*Lampropeltis getulus*
Scarlet King Snake	*Lampropeltis triangulum*
Coach Whip	*Masticophis flagellum flagellum*
Southern Water Snake	*Natrix sipedon fasciata*
Water Snake	*Matrix sipedon confluens*
Girard's Water Snake	*Natrix grahamii*
Diamondback Water Snake	*Natrix rhombifera*
Water Pilot	*Natrix taxispilota*
Bull Snake	*Pituophis sayi sayi*
Dekay's Snake	*Storeria dekayi*
Sand Snake	*Tantilla gracilis*
Marcy's Garter Snake	*Thamnophis marcianus*
Garter Snake	*Thamnophis sirtalis sirtalis*
Lined Snake	*Tropidoclonion lineatum*
*Coral Snake	*Micrurus fulvius fulvius*
*Copperhead	*Agkistrodon mokasen*
*Cottonmouth Moccasin	*Agkistrodon piscivorus*
*Canebrake Rattler	*Crotalus horridus atricaudaus*
*Timber Rattlesnake	*Crotalus horridus horridus*
*Ground Rattler	*Sistrurus miliarus miliarus*
Yellow Mud Turtle	*Kinosternon flavescens*
Keeled Mud Turtle	*Sternotherus carinatus*
Southern Musk Turtle	*Sternotherus odoratus*
Snapping Turtle	*Chelydra serpentina*
Alligator Snapping Turtle	*Macrochelys temminckii*
Gopher Tortoise	*Gopherus polyphemus*
Texas Terrapin	*Pseudemys texana*
Box Tortoise	*Terrapene major*
Soft-shelled Turtle	*Amyda mutica*

This list is compiled from the *Biological Survey of the East Texas Big Thicket.* An asterisk denotes a poisonous snake.

representative mammals of the big thicket

Florida Opossum	*Didelphis virginiana*

*Louisiana Bear	*Euarctos luteolus*
Raccoon	*Procyon lotor fuscipes*
Ringtail	*Bassariscus astutus*
Mink	*Mustela vison*
River Otter	*Lutra canadensis*
Gulf Spotted Skunk	*Spilogale putoris*
Striped Skunk	*Memphitus mephitus*
Red Fox	*Vulpes fulva*
Florida Gray Fox	*Urocyon cineroargenteus floridanus*
*Coyote	*Canis latrans*
*Texas Red Wolf	*Canis rufus*
*Panther	*Felis concolor*
Texas Bobcat	*Lynx rufus texensis*
Fox Squirrel	*Sciurur niger*
Grey Squirrel	*Sciurus carolensis carolensis*
Flying Squirrel	*Glaucomys volans*
Beaver	*Castor canadensis*
Muskrat	*Ondatra zibethicus*
Cottontail Rabbit	*Sylvilagus floridanus alacer*
Swamp Rabbit	*Sylvilagus aquaticus aquaticus*
Whitetailed Deer	*Odocoileus Virginianus texanus*
Nine-banded Armadillo	*Dasypus novemcinctus texanus*

This list was compiled from the *Biological Survey of the East Texas Big Thicket Area* and William B. Davis, *The Mammals of Texas,* Austin, Texas: Texas Parks and Wildlife Department, 1966. Asterisks indicate that a species is rare in the Big Thicket.

The entries in this appendix are not intended to be complete; they are intended to display the general nature of the life of the Big Thicket.

bibliography

Francis Edward Abernethy, *Tales From The Big Thicket*, Austin: University of Texas Press, 1966.

Ruth A. Allen, *East Texas Lumber Workers, An Economic and Social Picture, 1870-1950*, Austin: University of Texas Press, 1961.

Orrin H. Bonney, "Big Thicket—Biological Crossroads of North America," *The Living Wilderness*, V. 33, n. 106, Summer, 1969, pp. 19-21.

William T. Chambers, "Divisions of the Pine Forest Belt of East Texas," *Economic Geography*, v. 10, n. 3, July, 1934, pp. 302-318.

Carlton C. Curtis and S. C. Bausor, *The Complete Guide to North American Trees*, New York: Collier Books, 1943.

William B. Davis, *The Mammals of Texas*, Austin, Texas: Texas Parks and Wildlife Department, 1966.

W. E. S., Folsom-Dickerson, *The White Path*. 2nd Printing. San Antonio, Texas: The Naylor Company, 1965.

William O. Douglas, *Farewell to Texas, A Vanishing Wilderness*, New York: McGraw-Hill Book Company, 1967.

Dennis Farney, "Deciding on a 'Last True Wilderness,'" *Wall Street Journal*, July 1, 1968, p. 12.

"Geological Whodunit," *The Texaco Star*, Fall, 1946, pp. 22-23.

Ray Gill, "The Big Thicket of East Texas," *Beaumont Business*, May, 1938.

James C. Greenway, *Extinct and Vanishing Birds of the World*, New York: Dover Publications, Inc., 2nd ed., 1967.

William Carey Grimm, *The Book of Trees*, Harrisburg, Pensylvania, 1962.

Ludlow Griscom, Alexander Sprunt, *The Warblers of America*, New York: The Devin-Adair Company, 1957.

John A. Haislet, "National Champion Trees of Texas," Circular 86, Texas Forest Service, November, 1964.

Leon Augustus Hausman, *The Illustrated Encyclopedia of American Birds*, Garden City, New York: Garden City Publishing Company, Inc., 1947.

Dempsie Henley, *The Big Thicket Story*, Waco: Texian Press, 1967.

Dempsie Henley, *The Murder of Silence*, Waco: Texian Press, 1970.

Ed Holder, "Pocketful of Squirrels," *Texas Game and Fish*, Vol. 22, No. 1, January, 1966, pp. 4-5, 30. A biologically sponsored squirrel hunt in the Devil's Pocket.

Romeyn Beck Hough, *Handbook of the Trees of the Northern States and Canada*, Lowville, New York: Published by the Author, 1907.

Lamar State College of Technology, School of Education, *A Unit of the Big Thicket for Use on Sixth Grade Level*, Beaumont: The College, 1963.

Mary Lasswell, *I'll Take Texas*, Boston: Houghton Mifflin Company, 1958.

Gideon Lincecum, "Journal," MS, University of Texas Archives, #1263.

Cyrus Longworth Lundell, ed., *Contributions From the Texas Research Foundation*, Volume 1, Part 3, "The Oaks of Texas," by Cornelius H. Muller, Renner, Texas: Texas Research Foundation, 1951.

Claude A. McLeod, *The Big Thicket of East Texas*, Huntsville, Texas: the Sam Houston Press, 1967.

Frank Morris and Edward A. Eames, *Our Wild Orchids*, New York: Charles Scribner's Sons, 1929.

Frederick Law Olmstead, *A Journey Through Texas*, New York: Dix, Edwards & Co., 1857.

Lois Williams Parker, *Big Thicket Bibliography* (Big Thicket Museum Publication Series, No. 2), Saratoga, Texas: Big Thicket Museum, 1970.

H. B. Parks, "The Big Thicket," *Texas Geographic Magazine*, v. 2, n. 1, Summer, 1938, pp. 16-28.

H. B. Parks, "The Biogeography of East Texas" (Abstract), Proceedings and Transactions of the Texas Academy of Seience, Vol. 23, 1942, p. 42.

H. B. Parks "Research in Biotic Zones in Texas" (Abstract), Proceedings and Transactions of the Texas Academy of Science, Vol. 23, 1938-1939, pp. 43-44.

H. B. Parks, V. L. Cory and others, *Biological Survey of the East Texas Big Thicket Area*, Second Edition, 1932.

Wilbur F. Pate, "The Logging Industry at Diboll, Texas," Preceedings and Transactions of the Texas Academy of Science, Vol. 28, 1944, pp. 232-241.

Roger Tory Peterson, *A Field Guide to the Birds of Texas*, Boston: Houghton Mifflin Company, 1963.

Olin Sewall Pettingill, *A Guide to Bird Finding West of the Mississippi*, New York: Oxford University Press, 1953.

Caleb Pirtle III, "The Fight to Save Our Land and Heritage," *Southern Living*, v. 5, n. 3, May, 1970, pp. 48-49.

Richard J. Preston, Jr., *North American Trees*, Cambridge, Massachusetts: The M.I.T. Press, 1966.

Franklin M. Reck, "Big Thicket," *Frontier Times*, March, 1949, pp. 39-43.

Harold William Rickett, *Wild Flowers of the United States*, Vol. I, Part Two, The Southeastern States, New York: McGraw-Hill, 1967. (The Orchid Family, pp. 94-130)

Ellen D. Schulz and Robert Runyon, *Texas Cacti*, San Antonio: Texas Academy of Science, 1930.

Emma Mae Smelley, "Polk County, Texas—A Geographic Survey," *The Texas Geographic Magazine*, Vol. 9, No. 1, Spring, 1945, pp. 15-21. Describes the Big Thicket in the Southeastern part of the county.

Berton Roueché, "The Witness Tree," *The New Yorker*, August 31, 1968, pp. 56-64.

Benjamin Carroll Tharp, *Structure of Texas Vegetation East of the 98th Meridian*, University of Texas Bulletin No. 2606, Austin: University of Texas Press, 1926.

L. R. Wolfe, *Check-list of the Birds of Texas*, Lancaster Pennsylvania: Intelligencer Printing Company, 1956.

Solomon Alexander Wright, *My Rambles*, Arranged, with Introduction, by J. Frank Dobie, Austin: Texas Folklore Society, 1942.

index

a

b

163

Jackass, 23
Jackson, R. E., 69, 70, 71
Jaguar, 20
Jasmine, 63
Jasper County, 48
Javelina, 73
Johnson, President Lyndon B., 115
Jungle, 45, 48, 56, 135

k

Kaiser, Captain, 10
Kaiser's Burnout, 2
Karankawa Indians, 1
Kentucky, 55
King Ranch, 102
Kirby, John Henry, 11
Kirby Lumber, 130
Kirbyville, Texas, 11
Koasati (Coushatta) Indians, 3
Kountze News, 27
Kountze, Texas, xv, 27

l

Lace-lip spiral orchid, 38
Lasswell, Mary, 37
Lead arsenate, 94
Liberty County, 21, 52, 75
Life magazine, 129, 130
Lilly, Ben, 12
Lily, wild, 61
Lincecum, Gideon, 48
Lissie sands, 54
Little Cypress Creek Unit, 57, 62, cut 81
Little Pine Island Bayou, 52, 65

Little Thicket Association, 71
Live Oak, 101, 102
Livingston, Texas, 20, 54, 62, 95
Loblolly pine, 28, 60, 61, 89
    As indicator species, 45, 48
Loblolly Unit, 57-58, 96, 116
Long King's Village, 7
Longleaf pine, 29, 61
Louisiana, 28, 54, 106, 110, 130
Louisiana pine snake, 32
Lower Big Thicket, 47, 48, 52, 54, 62,
    63, 78, 87, 89
Lower Brazos Reserve, 3
Lufkin, Texas, 44, 84, 130
Lumbering, 10-12, 65-66, 82, 101, 106,
    110, 126, 130, 135-136
Lundell, Dr. C. L., 55

m

Maeir, Herbert, 70
Magnolia, xv, 38, 95, 96, 101, 130
    As indicator species, 45
    Pyramid magnolia, 29
    Sweetbay magnolia, 29
    Virgin, 81
    World's oldest, 94
Maple, 52
Marshall, C. B., 71
Maryland, 44
McDougal, W. B., 70
McLeod, Professor Claude A., 10, 44, 45,
    48, 52, 54, 78, 81
Menard Creek, 62, 63, 88, 116
Mesophytic, 45
Mesquite, 28
Mexican persimmon, 29
Mexico, 56
Mimosa, 29
Mink, 21
Mississippi, 29, 45, 48, 135
Mississippi Delta, 133

167

s

q

r

U

V

W